Foreword

THERE WERE TIMES when songfests, community sings and singing gatherings were all the rage. While there's still plenty of mileage left in those informal musical get-togethers, the contemporary musical shindig with the greatest drawing power is the hootenanny. Until recently non-members of the in-group of the folk-music world were justly perplexed by this whatchamacallit kind of word. But thanks to the 20th-century folk song revival, television and the popular record business, it's pretty hard to find anyone who hasn't seen, or at least heard of, a hootenanny.

Before folk-music people adopted hootenanny it had been one of those good old all-purpose American words that could stand for anything either unmentionable or forgotten during a temporary lapse of memory as in *get off your hootenanny* or *hand me the hootenanny*. It had seen considerable service in the Southwest and Midwest as a name for a party which just sort of happened without being planned. And it was that party usage which led to the introduction of the term to folk-song performers.

In the summer of 1940 some local political leaders from Seattle were looking for a name to pin on a series of fund-raising parties they were planning. Since the parties were to be of an impromptu nature featuring everything from dinners and dancing to entertainment, door prizes and uncertainty, the hootenanny tag was a natural. Credit for getting the right name to the right place at the right time goes to Terry Pettus who remembered it from his Hoosier youth. Pete Seeger and Woody Guthrie picked up the idea in Seattle and took it back to New York where they attached it to their Sunday afternoon singing gatherings. By the time those Sunday afternoon hoots had worked their way up from rent-paying homespun affairs to Carnegie Hall the hootenanny was an established folk-music term. The usage was academically confirmed in 1959 when the dictionaries began to include it.

As might be expected, critics subsequently began arguing as to precisely what kind of affair was technically a hootenanny. Some argued that if certain people were picked to sing it was a hoot—but if anyone and everyone could pick and sing it wasn't. Fortunately there were enough people around who didn't give a hoot about such hair-splitting so that common usage has remained uncomplicated and general in meaning.

Hootenanny Tonight! was prepared in the traditional spirit of the hoot. It's an impromptu wing-ding full of old friends and new, and a few surprises. It just happened—there was no plan. The songs are those I have met over and over again at the hoots I've been involved in the past few years. The notes accompanying the songs are intended to convey information, ideas and record references that will help you understand, interpret and perform the songs more interestingly, effectively and creatively yourself.

Spontaneity and creativity have been essential ingredients in a vital folk-music tradition. We can keep our tradition vital by avoiding slavish imitation of others and by using ourselves to show how good the songs are instead of the songs to show how good we are. More power to you if you use this collection as a springboard to doing things your own way.

I am grateful to many performers for their help and co-operation in the preparation of this book. I have acknowledged their help in the headnotes to the songs. However, I feel particularly indebted to Irwin Silber of *Sing Out* magazine for his cooperation and advice. Over the years, I have found *Sing Out* to be an extremely valuable source of ideas, information and just plain gossip about the world of folk music. If this sounds like a plug, that's exactly what it's meant to be. I enthusiastically recommend *Sing Out* to everyone who enjoys this book. (Please write to Sing Out, Inc., 165 West 46th Street, New York 36, N. Y., for more information.)

They say no one but an author reads a foreword. If this is not true, forgive me for delaying you on your way to the bluegrass, hillbilly, blues, traditional ballads, love songs, spirituals and gospel songs, chanteys and just plain folk songs in the pages that follow.

—JAMES F. LEISY

HOOTENNANY
TONIGHT!

by James F. Leisy

An Original Gold Medal Book

GOLD MEDAL BOOKS

FAWCETT PUBLICATIONS, INC., GREENWICH, CONN.

MEMBER OF AMERICAN BOOK PUBLISHERS COUNCIL, INC.

Contents
Alphabetical by titles

Mama Don't Allow

Ma - ma don't al - low no pick-in' and a-grin-nin' 'round here._____ Ma-ma don't al-low no pick-in' and grin-nin' 'round here._____ Now, we don't care what ma - ma don't al - low Do some pick-in' and a-grin-nin' an - y - how Ma - ma don't al - low no pick-in' and a-grin-nin' 'round here._____

Born out of some real rehearsal problems, I'm sure, this country classic has been a favorite of just about every kind of group I've ever played with from Dixieland to Hillbilly to Folk. It would be easy to say that the version given here is "the one we used to always do," but it wouldn't be true. No group I've ever played with did this number the same way twice. Just like a hootenanny itself, it's impossible to predict where you're going and how it will all end once you've started. There's always plenty that mama won't allow born out of the scene you're making at the moment—and there's no reason to confine her prohibitions to the instruments in the group, though that's traditional and a fine way to get started. You can hear many different versions of ''Mama'' on records by Dixieland, Hillbilly and Folk groups but I don't recommend any of them. I'm sure that everyone who ever made a record of this song would agree with me that the performance was sterile. It's a jam session piece that really doesn't mean a thing without the spontaneity, goofs and horseplay of an off-the-record rendition. Here are a few verse ideas to get you started; after that you're on your own:

Mama don't allow no guitar pickin' around here.
Mama don't allow no guitar pickin' around here.
We don't care what mama don't allow;
Gonna pick that guitar anyhow.
Mama don't allow no guitar pickin' around here.

Mama don't allow no banjo strummin' around here.
Mama don't allow no banjo strummin' around here.
We don't care what mama don't allow;
Gonna flog that banjo anyhow.
Mama don't allow no banjo strummin' around here.

Bass bumpin'—drum bangin'—loud playin'—soft playin'—sad playin' (switch to A minor using Am, E7, and Dm instead of the regular chords)—fiddle fiddlin'—foot stompin'—twistin' music—piano plunkin'—mistakes (make 'em)—hillbilly—dixie—bossa nova (or whatever it is). Incidentally, it's customary to weave the instrumental part in and out of each verse as it is sung. For example, the fiddle player fiddles during his verse on the third and fourth measures, seventh and eighth measures, and the last two measures. He can also fiddle throughout measures 9 through 12 with or without those lines being sung, according to the preference of the group. Each verse is followed by an appropriate instrumental chorus without singing.

Nine Hundred Miles

Well, I'm walk-ing down this track; I've got tears in my eyes, Try'n to read a let-ter from my home.___ And if this train runs me right I'll be home to-mor-row night 'cause I'm nine hun-dred miles from my home,___ And I hate to hear that lone-some whis-tle blow.___

I will pawn you my watch;
I will pawn you my chain;
Pawn you my gold diamond ring.
And if this train runs me right
I'll be home tomorrow night
'Cause I'm nine hundred miles from my home,
And I hate to hear that lonesome whistle blow.

Adapted and arranged by Cisco Houston. Copyright Stormking Music, Inc. Used by permission.

If my woman tells me so,
I will railroad no more;
I'll hang around her shanty all the time.
And if this train runs me right
I'll be home tomorrow night
'Cause I'm nine hundred miles from my home,
And I hate to hear that lonesome whistle blow.

Now this train I ride on
Is a hundred coaches long;
Travels back a hundred miles or more;
And if this train runs me right
I'll be home tomorrow night,
'Cause I'm nine hundred miles from my home,
And I hate to hear that lonesome whistle blow.

This haunting hillbilly railroad song has some sort of brother-sister relationship to the unique blues waltz, "In the Pines." It has been pretty popular with the commercial folk-style singers and there are several present-day adaptations and re-writes. Although something might be said for all of them (printable and otherwise), you're not likely to get any criticism from the "ethnics" for this earlier version I learned from George Williams. Listen to Sam Hinton (Decca, DL 8108), Cisco Houston (Folkways, FA 2013), and Dan Isaacson (Cornell, CRS 10021).

Whiskey In The Jar
(Kilgary Mountain)

As I was a walk - in' 'round Kil - gar - y Moun - tain,___ I met Colo - nel Pep - per and his mon - ey he was count - in',___ I rat - tled___ me pis - tols and I drew forth me sa - ber, Say - in', "Stand and de - liv - er, for I am the bold de - ceiv - er!" Mush - a rig um du rum da, Whack fol __ the dad - dy O, Whack fol __ the dad - dy O, There's whis - key in the jar.

The shining golden coins did look so bright and jolly,
I took 'em with me home and I gave 'em to my Molly;
She promised and she vowed that she never would
    deceive me,
But the devil's in the women and they never can be easy.

When I was awakened between six and seven,
The guards were all around me in numbers odd and
    even;
I flew to my pistols, but alas, I was mistaken,
For Molly'd drawn my pistols and a prisoner I was
    taken.

They put me in jail without judge or writin',
For robbing Colonel Pepper on Kilgary Mountain,
But they didn't take my fists so I knocked the sentry
    down,
And bid a fond farewell to the jail in Slaigo town.

Now, some take delight in fishin' and bowlin',
And others take delight in their carriages a-rollin',
But I take delight in the juice of the barley,
And courtin' pretty girls in the mornin' so early.

This is a popular American version of an equally popular
Irish street ballad. An Irish version from the 1870's
appears in Colm O'Lochlainn's *Irish Street Ballads* with
a different tune and ending to the story. Since there is
no Kilgary Mountain in Ireland you may wish to refer
to the far-famed Kerry Mountain instead. Commercial
folk-style singers (The Limeliters) popularized an "arranged" version of this up-tempo song in the early
1960's.

Hey Lidee

Chorus

Hey Li - dee, Li - dee, Li - dee,— Hey Li - dee, Li - dee - lo.—

Hey Li - dee, Li - dee, Li - dee,— Hey Li - dee, Li - dee - lo.—

Verse

This is a craz - y kind of song,— Hey Li - dee, Li - dee - lo.— You make it up as you go a - long,— Hey Li - dee, Li - dee - lo.—

First you sing a simple line,
Hey Lidee, Lidee-lo.
Then you try to make it rhyme,
Hey Lidee, Lidee-lo.

While you catch on I'll sing a verse,
Then you do one that's even worse.

The singer you fast the getter it's tough,
To line up makes that you won't muff.

I know a girl who lives on a hill,
She won't fool around but her sister will.

I know a girl who lives in Greenwich Village,
She won't fool around but her brother will.

Your secret's safe with a married man;
Single men talk—all they can.

Whenever somebody breaks out this old campus favorite
you can figure the party's going to get a little rough.
Bill Strub of Minneapolis holds the unofficial marathon
record for making up fresh and unprintable verses on the
spot without ever missing a beat. At a wing-ding in
Sausalito in 1959 he won a sizable bet by lasting for 57
minutes—which is quite an accomplishment when you
consider that one of the conditions was the verses be
continuously entertaining! As you can see from the
verses printed here (pun intended), this song is at its
best when you make up verses as you go along. A live,
spontaneous performance by The Limeliters at the Ash
Grove in Hollywood has been preserved on their LP,
Tonight In Person, The Limeliters (RCA Victor, LPM-
2272).

Sing the chorus a couple of times to get everyone
warmed up and then use some of the sample verses shown
here, if you need them, to help you get started. Then let
everyone take turns making up his own verses calypso
style. Everyone joins in on the chorus after each verse
and on the ''Hey Lidee'' lines in the verses. Some people
use Loddee, Lilee, or Lollee instead of Lidee. Since the
words are there for sound rather than meaning it doesn't
really matter what you use.

The Gypsy Rover

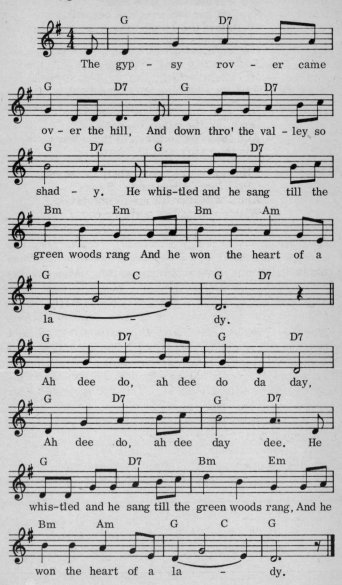

The gyp - sy rov - er came ov - er the hill, And down thro' the val - ley so shad - y. He whis-tled and he sang till the green woods rang And he won the heart of a la - dy.

Ah dee do, ah dee do da day, Ah dee do, ah dee day dee. He whis-tled and he sang till the green woods rang, And he won the heart of a la - dy.

She left her father's castle gate;
She left her own true lover;
She left her servants and her estate
To follow the gypsy rover.

Her father saddled his fastest steed
And roamed the valley all over.
He sought his daughter at great speed,
And the whistling gypsy rover.

He came at last to a mansion fine
Down by the River Clayde;
And there was music and there was wine
For the gypsy and his lady.

"He's no gypsy, my father," said she,
"He's lord of freelands all over;
And I will stay till my dying day
With my whistling gypsy rover."

The famous ballad that tells the story of the gypsy who charms a highborn lady into leaving her home has been handed down in several popular forms. Almost every schoolboy has sung the "Wraggle Taggle Gypsies" version, and Woody Guthrie won a lot of popularity for the "Gypsy Davey" version. Good as those versions are they just don't measure up to this lilting variant that has been popular for many years in Great Britain and this country, though less well-known than the two named above. If you're a good whistler you will want to vary the choruses by whistling some of the melody and singing the rest. Tommy Makem's rendition of "The Gypsy Rover" at the Newport Folk Festival in 1960 is preserved on a Vanguard LP (VRS 9083).

Midnight Special

Chorus

Let the mid - night spec - ial ___
Shine it's light ___ on me.
___ Let the mid - night spec - ial ___
___ Shine it's ev - er - lov - in' light on me. ___

Verse

___ Well, you wake up in the
morn - ing, ___ hear the ding ___ dong
ring. ___ You go march - in' to the
tab - le ___ see the same ___ old ___
thing. Well, it's on - a the ___ tab - le, ___

18

Knife, a fork, and a pan.

If you say a thing a - bout it

You're in troub-le with the man.

2. If you ever go to Houston, you better walk right,
   You better not stagger, and you better not fight.
   Sheriff Benson will arrest you, and he'll carry you
       down,
   You can bet your bottom dollar, you're sugarland
       bound.

3. Yonder come Doc Melton, tell me how do you know?
   He gave me a tablet just the day before.
   There never was a doctor travelin' over the land
   That could cure the fever of a convict man.

4. Yonder comes Miss Rosy, tell me how do you know?
   I know her by her apron, and the dress that she
       wore,
   Umbrella on her shoulder, piece of paper in her
       hand,
   She says to the captain, "I want my lifetime man!"

This is probably the most popular of the prison blues
among folk-song enthusiasts. It is usually sung at a
brisk tempo. At that tempo and with its standardized pop-
song form instead of the simpler traditional blues form,
it is much less recognizable to the average person as a
blues.

According to prison legend a man would go free if the
headlight of this train would shine through his bars on
him.

Brown's Ferry Blues

Hard luck pop-pa a-count-in' his toes, You can smell his feet wher-ev-er he goes. Lord, Lord, and he's got those Brown's Fer-ry Blues.

Hard luck pop-pa done lost his stuff; The troub-le with him he's played too rough. Lord, Lord, and he's got those Brown's Fer-ry Blues.

Two old maids a-sitting in the sand;
Each one wishing that the other was a man.
Lord, Lord, got those Brown's Ferry Blues.
Two old maids done lost their style.
If you want to be lucky you got to smile.
Lord, Lord, got those Brown's Ferry Blues.

Early to bed and early to rise;
And your girl goes out with other guys.
Lord, Lord, got those Brown's Ferry Blues.
If you don't believe me, try it yourself;
Well, I tried it and I got left.
Lord, Lord, got those Brown's Ferry Blues.

Hardluck poppa standing in the rain;
If the world was corn he couldn't buy grain.
Lord, Lord, got those Brown's Ferry Blues.
Hard luck poppa standing in the snow;
His knees knock together but he's rarin' to go.
Lord, Lord, got those Brown's Ferry Blues.

I visited with John Cohen of The New Lost City Ramblers at the Ash Grove in Los Angeles soon after The Rooftop Singers had released a folknik version of the "Tom Cat Blues," which The Ramblers had recorded earlier for Folkways Records LP (FA 2396). Since The Rooftop Singers had made it big with "Walk Right In" just before that, it was beginning to look like they could go right on living at the top of the heap by re-recording old commercial hillbilly records forever. At that time John thought that "Brown's Ferry Blues" might be the next one on the list since it had appeared in the same LP with "Tom Cat Blues." So far nothing has happened but that doesn't mean it won't. In the meantime, this amalgamation of Negro blues, jazz and minstrelsy that became a fairly staple item in hillbilly repertoires in its day, still has plenty of action left in it. For strictly country versions you'll have to track down the McGee Brothers on Decca or the Delmore Brothers on Bluebird or head for the backwoods for a live rendition.

Raise A Ruckus

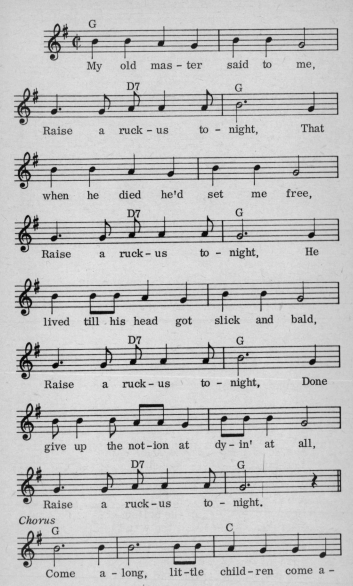

My old mas-ter said to me,

Raise a ruck-us to-night, That

when he died he'd set me free,

Raise a ruck-us to-night, He

lived till his head got slick and bald,

Raise a ruck-us to-night, Done

give up the not-ion at dy-in' at all,

Raise a ruck-us to-night.

Chorus

Come a-long, lit-tle child-ren come a-

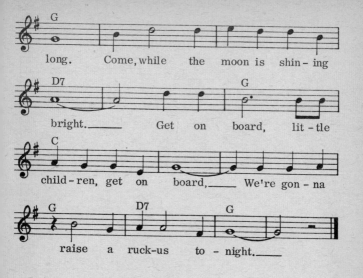

long. Come, while the moon is shin-ing
bright.___ Get on board, lit-tle
child-ren, get on board,___ We're gon-na
raise a ruck-us to-night.___

My old mistress said to me,
Raise a ruckus tonight,
That when she died she'd set me free,
Raise a ruckus tonight.

Now she's makin' out her will,
Raise a ruckus tonight,
To leave me plowin' yonder hill,
Raise a ruckus tonight.

Continue, as above:

That's what they done promised me,
But they died too slow for me.
A dose of poison helped them along,
And the devil preached their funeral song.

Way down yonder in Chitlin' Switch
A bullfrog jumped from ditch to ditch;
Jumped way down in the bottom of a well,
Swore he'd jumped all the way to hell.

Some folks say a preacher won't steal.
I caught two in my cornfiel'.
One had a bushel; one had fo';
If that ain't stealin', I don't know.

Rufus Akes and Rastus Payne;
They got married down in Gaines.
Now they say them Georgia woods
Is full of Akes and Paynes.

I'm going down to the river now;
I'll lay me down and then I'll die.
But if I find the water's wet,
I'll have to wait until it's dry.

"Raise a Ruckus," usually pronounced "rookus," was
popular with Negro minstrels who sang on street corners,
at medicine shows, and at fairs, holidays and picnics. The
Negro minstrel operated more in the traditional minstrel manner, in which one or more musicians travel from
place to place performing wherever and whenever anyone would underwrite their performance. He was dis-
tinct from the black-faced minstrel of the vaudeville
circuit, though probably somewhat influenced by him.
The first verses are more recent and emphasize the protest aspects of this song. They are the ones most frequently used by contemporary folk-style singers. The
rest of the verses which I have picked up from here,
there, and everywhere, are from the Negro minstrel tradition.

Good News

Chorus

Good news!

Talk a - bout your good news:

Char - i - ot's a - com - in', Good

Char - i - ot's a - com - in',

news!

Sing a - bout the news: The

Char - i - ot's a - com - in', Good

Char - i - ot's a - com - in'

news!

Shout a - bout your good news:

Char - i - ot's a - com - in', And I

Char - i - ot's a - com - in', And I

G   D7   G
don't want it to leave me be - hind.

don't want it to leave me be - hind.

G
There's a long white robe in

heav- en I know,

There's a long white robe in

There's a

heav - en I know, There's a

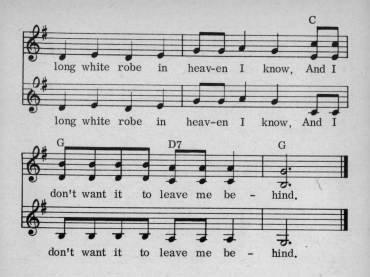

long white robe in heav-en I know, And I

long white robe in heav-en I know, And I

don't want it to leave me be - hind.

don't want it to leave me be - hind.

Continue, as above:

> **There's a pair of wings in heaven I know.**
> **There's a starry crown in heaven I know.**
>
> **There's a golden harp in heaven I know.**
>
> **It's a better place than this world I know.**

Here is a simple three-part arrangement for group singing of this popular gospel spiritual. If you want to sing it solo you'll find the melody mostly in the bottom notes of the top line. It moves around a little in the verses, but should be easy to locate. For both solo and choral performances listen to Lee Charles (Riverside, RLP 12-651), Bob Gibson (Riverside, RLP 12-816), and the Howard University Choir (RCA Victor, LM 2126).

The Wreck Of The F. F. V.

A - long came the F. F. V._____ The swift - est on the line._____ Roar - ing down the C and O Road_____ And twen - ty min - utes be - hind._____ Run - ning in - to Sou - ville_____ head-quar - ters on the line._____ Re-ceiv - ing their strict or - ders_____ From a sta - tion just be - hind._____

George Alley's mother came to him
With a basket on her arm.
She said to him, "My darling son,
Be careful how you run.
Many a man has lost his life
In tryin' to make up lost time;
But if you run this engine right
You'll get there just on time."

Then up the road the engine sped
Till against a rock she crashed.
Upside down the engine turned
And Georgie's breast did smash.
His head against the firebox lay
As the burning flames rolled o'er.
"I'm glad I was born an engineer
To die on the C and O Road."

The doctor said to Georgie:
"My darling boy, lie still.
Your life may yet be saved
If it be God's blessed will."
"Oh, no, dear Doc, that cannot be,
I want to die so free.
I want to die with the engine I love,
Number one hundred and forty-three."

The doctor said to Georgie:
"Your life cannot be saved.
Murdered upon the railroad
And laid in a lonesome grave."
His face was covered up with blood,
His eyes you could not see.
And the very last words poor Georgie said
Was "Nearer my God to Thee."

On October 23, 1890 the Fast Flying Vestibule of the
C & O Railroad Line, with George Alley running Engine
143, ran into a pile of rocks near Hinton, West Virginia,
and crashed. This popular hillbilly ballad tells the story
of that tragic event. Known by several titles, including
"The Wreck on the C & O Road" and "Engine 143," it
is a favorite in the folk-song tradition of the southern
mountain country. The RCA Victor recording of the
version by the famous Carter Family in 1927, was probably the most popular one ever made. The original Carter

Family version is in the *Anthology of American Folk Music,* Volume I (Folkways, FA 2951). You may also look up two other distinctively different versions by The Kossoy Sisters (Tradition, TLP 1018) and Joan Baez (Vanguard, VRS 9094). I picked up this version from Preacher Jack Thornton, a wild-eyed banjo player from Missouri, Texas and California (in that order).

Mama, Mama, Have You Heard?

It's not unusual at a hoot for someone to come up with a humorous treatment or parody of a well-known song. This parody of "Hush, Little Baby" has enlivened several sessions I've attended. Daddy's final reaction is not necessarily as mild as the one I have indicated.

Ma-ma, ma-ma, have you heard,
Dad-dy's gon-na buy me a mock-ing-bird;
If that mock-ing-bird won't sing,
Dad-dy's gon-na buy me a dia-mond ring.

> If the diamond's not okay,
> Daddy's gonna buy me a **Chevrolet;**
> If that **Chevrolet** won't run,
> Daddy's gonna buy me a **B-B gun.**
>
> If that **B-B gun** won't shoot,
> Daddy's gonna buy me a swimming suit;
> If that swimming suit don't fit,
> Daddy's gonna say, "Oh, gee, I quit!"

Lord Randall

Oh,— where have you been,— Lord Ran-dall, my son? Where have you been,— oh my pret-ty one? I've been to my sweet-heart, moth-er, I've been to my sweet-heart, moth-er. Make my bed soon for I'm sick to my heart And I fain would lie down.

Oh, what did you have for your supper, my son?
What did you have, oh my pretty one?
A cup of cold poison, mother.
A cup of cold poison, mother.
Make my bed soon for I'm sick to my heart
And I fain would lie down.

Continue, as above:

Oh, what will you leave your father, my son?
My wagon and oxen, mother.

→

Oh, what will you leave your mother, my son?
My house and my lands.

Oh, what will you leave your brother, my son?
My horn and my hounds.

Oh, what will you leave your sister, my son?
The rings on my fingers.

Oh, what will you leave your sweetheart, my son?
A rope that will hang her.

Folk-song scholars have traced this famous ballad all over Europe and America and have found many different melodic and textual variations. The 19th century ballad scholar, Francis James Child, found that it had been popular in Italy for over three hundred years. Some folk-song specialists have conjectured that the popular song, "Billy Boy" is a parody or burlesque of the ballad. The variant presented here is the most popular accompanied version in this country. There is a different melodic version which is favored for unaccompanied singing. For several different interpretations listen to Paul Clayton (Folkways, FA 2110), John Jacob Niles (RCA Camden, CAL 330), Pete Seeger (Folkways, FA 2439), Josh White (Decca, DL 8665), Harry Belafonte (RCA Victor, LPM 1022), and Richard Dyer-Bennet (Stinson, SLP 61).

The Cherry Tree Carol

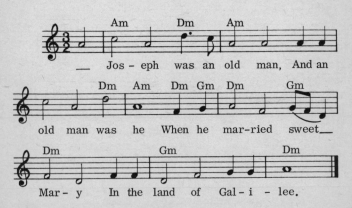

Jos - eph was an old man, And an old man was he When he mar-ried sweet Mar - y In the land of Gal - i - lee.

Joseph and Mary walked through an orchard good,
There were cherries and berries as red as your blood.

Oh, then up spoke Mary, so meek and so mild,
"Pluck me one cherry, Joseph, for I am with child."

And then up spoke Joseph with words most unkind,
"Let him pluck thee a cherry that brought thee with
    child."

Oh, then up spoke the babe within his mother's womb,
"Bow down the tallest tree, for my mother to have
    some."

Then bowed down the tallest tree unto his mother's
    hand;
Then she cried, "See, Joseph, I have cherries at my
    command."

Oh, then up spoke Joseph, "I have done Mary wrong;
But cheer up my dearest, and be not cast down."

Then Mary plucked a cherry, as red as your blood,
Then Mary went home with her heavy load.

Then Mary took her babe, and sat him on her knee,
She said, "My dear son, tell me what with this world
    will be."

"Oh, I shall be as dead, mother, as the stones in the wall;
And the people in the streets, mother, shall mourn for
    me all."
"Upon Easter day, mother, my uprising shall be;
And the sun and the moon, mother, shall both rise with
    me."

This version of what may be the most popular Christmas
ballad known today is from the southern mountain re-
gion of the United States. I am particularly fond of the
haunting, spiritual quality of the melody. For several
different versions listen to Isla Cameron (Tradition, TLP
1001), Cynthia Gooding (Elektra, EKL 107), Josef and
Miranda Marais (Decca, DL 9030), Peggy, Barbara,
and Penny Seeger (Folkways, FC 7053), and Paul Clayton (Folkways, FA 2310).

Wildwood Flower

I will twine and will min - gle my wav - ing black hair with the ro - ses so red and the li - ly so fair. The myr - tle so green of an em - er-ald hue, The pale em-an-i - ta and eyes look like blue.

Oh he promised to love me,
He promised to love,
To cherish me always
All others above.
I woke from my dream
And my idol was clay,
My passion for loving
Had vanished away.

I'll dance and I'll sing
And my life shall be gay,
I'll charm every heart
In the crowd I survey;
Though my heart now is breaking,
He never shall know
How his name makes me tremble,
My pale cheeks to glow.

Oh, he taught me to love him,
He called me his flower,
A blossom to cheer him
Through life's weary hour.
But now he has gone
And left me alone,
The wild flowers to weep
And the wild birds to moan.

I'll dance and I'll sing
And my heart will be gay,
I'll banish this weeping,
Drive troubles away,
I'll live yet to see him
Regret this dark hour,
When he won and neglected
This frail wildwood flower.

This great tune has long been a favorite of backwoods guitar pickers. When a guitar player graduates from using simple strums to accompany songs and begins to explore the fascinating world of melody picking, this is usually one of the first songs he tries. The tune is especially easy to pick out on the guitar in the key of C, because so many of the notes fall on open strings, strings fretted to form the chord, and neighboring frets. If you're a pretty good strummer and you're looking for new fields to conquer, you should give it a try and find out how easy it really is. There are many good recordings of this popular hillbilly song. Lester Flatt and Earl Scruggs have given it a good going over with their educated fingers. Folkways has three good recordings on LP's by Mickey Miller (FA 2393), Artus Moser (FA 2112), and Eugene and Veronica Cox (FA 2314). The lyric may seem a little soupy to some; apparently it struck Woody Guthrie that way, for he ignored the words altogether when he borrowed the tune for his World War II disaster ballad, "Reuben James."

Ah-Hah-Hah

In the spring of 1963 I attended one of the wildest hoots ever, in Fresno, California. It started with two guitars and one bottle at five o'clock on a Friday afternoon and ended two days later, folk song aficionados having gathered from all over. Somewhere in the middle of all the chaos a Canadian girl appeared from nowhere and stopped us all cold with her rendition of this song and several others. She disappeared as mysteriously as she appeared, but not before I prevailed on her to write the words down on the back of the room service menu. Whoever she is, wherever she is, thanks a lot for a heckuva good song.

My moth-er chose my hus-band, a law-yer's son was he, And on our wed-ding night he came to bed with me. Ah - hah - hah, that's no way to Ah - hah - hah, that can't be.

And on the wedding night he came to bed with me.
He bit me on the shoulder and nearly broke my knee.

He bit me on the shoulder and nearly broke my knee.
I called my waiting woman, "Come quickly, Marjorie."

Continue as above, repeating first the last line from the previous verse:

"Go tell mamá I'm dying. Bid her come hastily."

Come, mamá, to my bedside before I could count three.

"Cheer up, my girl, what ails you will never kill," said
    she.

"If I had died of that, child, God knows where you
    would be."

"So if you die, my daughter, I'll grave you splendidly."

"And write upon your tombstone for all the world to
    see."

"The only girl that ever died of that malady."

I Am A Pilgrim

This traditional gospel favorite really swings. Be sure to use the blue notes in the fourth and twelfth measures. There is a good recording by Obray Ramsay in his Riverside album (RLP 12-649).

I got a mother, a sister, and a brother,
Who have gone to that sweet land.
I'm determined to go and see them, good Lord,
All over on that distant shore.

As I go down to that river of Jordan,
Just to bathe my weary soul,
If I could touch but the hem of His garment, good Lord,
Well, I believe it would make me whole.

Kum Ba Ya

This lullaby-like song is very popular among folk-song enthusiasts and in schools and children's camps. I've been told the song originated in the southern United States and traveled to Africa, where this fragmentary version became traditional. According to this same legend the lyrics are an attempt to imitate the words "come by here." A few years ago this song was "found" in Africa and brought back to the U.S., where it has now become part of our tradition. As the world gets smaller and cultures mix, more of this sort of tradition-swapping is bound to take place. The words are pronounced *koom bah yah* and the song is sung very slowly with dignity. The Weavers have their own version in which they have added English verses.

I'm A Rambler

I'm partial to songs with an interlude quality that can be performed effectively without an obvious ending. This song and "I Know Where I'm Going" are my two favorites of this kind. You will notice the melody ends on an E7 chord and that it cries out for resolution to the tonic chord (A) of the song. As you sing each verse the tension is resolved when the melody returns to the tonic in the second measure. When you get to the last verse you may be unable to resist the urge to follow the E7 chord with an A chord while you are holding the last tone of the song, but if you can you may find it intriguing to end there or taper off instrumentally by running through the chords of the song and still ending on the seventh. If you do you will establish the effect of leaving the story "up in the air" with the implication that there is either more to follow, someday, or that all of the story has not been told.

The story here is from the same family of songs that has given us "On Top of Old Smoky," "The Wagoner's Lad," "The Cuckoo," "Jack of Diamonds," and "Rye Whiskey." You will notice the relationships in the verses.

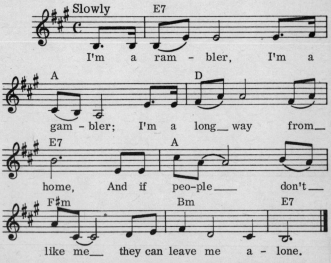

It's dark and it's raining
And the moon gives no light.
My pony won't travel
A dark road at night.

Oh, come feed your horses;
Come feed them some hay;
Come sit down beside me
Just as long as you stay.

My horses aren't hungry;
They won't eat your hay;
I'm going to Wyoming;
I'll graze on the way.

I once had a sweetheart;
Her age was sixteen;
She was the flower of Bolton
And the belle of Saline.

Her parents were against me;
Now she is the same;
If I'm in your book, love,
Please blot out my name.

There are changes in the ocean.
There are changes in the sea.
There are changes in my true love;
But there's no change in me.

The Blues Ain't Nothin' But A Good Man Feelin' Bad

That's all—in this song that follows the simplest traditional twelve-bar blues form. I picked up this version in Texas in the 1930's.

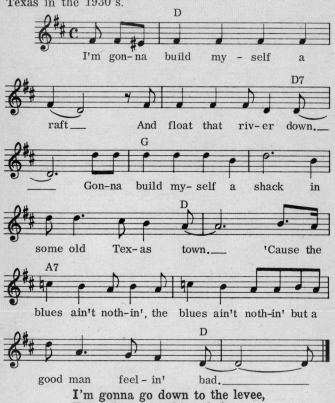

I'm gon-na build my-self a raft___ And float that riv-er down.___ ___ Gon-na build my-self a shack in some old Tex-as town.___ 'Cause the blues ain't noth-in', the blues ain't noth-in' but a good man feel-in' bad._____

I'm gonna go down to the levee,
Take along a rockin' chair.
If my baby don't come to see me,
Gonna rock away from there.
'Cause the blues ain't nothin'
The blues ain't nothin'
But a good man feelin' bad.

Now, when my baby said good-by,
Had to break right down and cry.
When my baby said good-by,

I thought I'd surely die.
Oh, the blues ain't nothin'
No, the blues ain't nothin'
But a good man feelin' bad.

We Wish You A Merry Christmas

This old English carol ranks with "The Twelve Days of Christmas" in popularity for Christmas hoots. In door-to-door work it enables singers to make a somewhat subtle request for dry-throat relief. The Weavers have recorded it on a Vanguard album (VRS 9013) and Alan Mills recorded it for Folkways (FP 709).

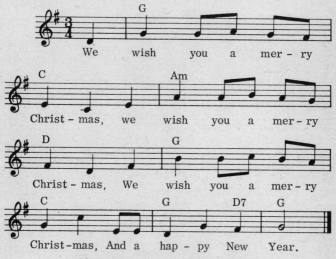

We wish you a mer - ry
Christ - mas, we wish you a mer - ry
Christ - mas, We wish you a mer - ry
Christ - mas, And a hap - py New Year.

Oh, bring us some figgy pudding,
Oh, bring us some figgy pudding,
Oh, bring us some figgy pudding,
With a cup of good cheer.

As above:

We won't go until we get it,
So bring it out here.

We all love our figgy pudding
With a cup of good cheer.

We wish you a merry Christmas
And a happy New Year.

43

The Billboard Song

This silly song may be one of the earliest singing commercials still making the rounds. It has provided a lot of free advertising for various enterprises over the years. The song has been updated several times for contemporary audiences. Probably the most popular of the more recent versions was created by Charles Grean for a hit record by Homer and Jethro a few years back. I'm indebted to Jim McDaniel of Sausalito, California, for this anachronistic version that has enlivened many a hoot

As I was walk-ing down the street A
bill-board caught my eye. The ad-ver-tise-ment
writ-ten there would make you laugh and cry. The
wind and rain had come that day And
washed it half a-way. And what was left upon that sign, It made the bill-board say:

Come smoke a Coca-Cola,
Chew catsup cigarettes;
See Lillian Russell wrestle
With a box of oysterettes;
Good pork and beans will meet tonight
In a finish fight.

Chauncey Depew will lecture
On sapolio tonight.

Bay rum is good for horses;
It is the best in town.
Castoria cures the measles;
You pay five dollars down.
Teeth extracted without pain
For the price of half a dime.
Overcoats are selling now
A little out of time.

Chew Wrigley's for that headache,
Take Campbell's for that cough;
There's going to be a swimming meet
In the village watering trough.
Buy a case of ginger ale,
It makes the best of broth.
Shinola's sure to curl the hair
And not to take it off.

Barbara Allen

In Scar-let town where I was born There lived a fair young maid-en. She was the fair-est of them all, And her name was Bar-b'ry Al-len.

'Twas in the merry month of May,
When flowers were a-bloomin',
Sweet Willie on his deathbed lay
For the love of Barb'ry Allen.

He sent his servant to the town,
The town that she did dwell in,
Saying, "Master bid me to come here,
If your name be Barb'ry Allen."

Then slowly, slowly she rose up,
And slowly she went to him,
And all she said when she got there:
"Young man, I think you're dyin'."

"Oh, yes, I'm sick within my heart,
And I never will get better,
Until I know the love of one,
The love of Barb'ry Allen."

"Oh, don't you remember the other day,
When we were in the tavern,
You drank a toast to the ladies all,
But you slighted Barb'ry Allen."

"Oh, yes, I know, I know it well,
When we were in the tavern,
I gave a toast to the ladies all,
But my love to Barb'ry Allen."

He turned his face unto the wall,
And death was with him dealin'.
"Adieu, adieu, to all my friends,
Be kind to Barb'ry Allen."

Then lightly she tripped down the stairs
He trembled like an aspen.
" 'Tis vain, 'tis vain, my dear young man
To hone for Barb'ry Allen."

She walked out in the green, green fields,
She heard his death bell knellin'.
And every stroke they seemed to say:
"Hardhearted Barb'ry Allen."

She looked to the east; she looked to the west;
She saw his corpse a-comin',
"Oh, set him down for me," she cried,
"That I may gaze upon him."

The more she looked the more she grieved,
Until she burst out cryin';
Saying, ''Pick me up and carry me home,
For I feel like I am dyin'.''

''Oh, father, dear, go dig my grave;
Go dig it deep and narrow.
Sweet Willie died for me today;
I'll die for him tomorrow.''

They buried Willie in the old churchyard
And Barb'ry in the new one.
From Willie's grave there grew a rose;
From Barb'ry's a green brier.

They grew and grew to the old church wall
Till they couldn't grow no higher;
And there they tied in a true-love knot,
The rose bush and the brier.

Here is another one of the ''giants'' among the British
ballads that have remained universally appealing for several centuries. I learned this particular version from
George Williams of Portola Valley, California and believe it to be the most melodically singable that I have
ever heard. There is hardly a single contemporary folk-
style singer who has not recorded some version of this
ballad. You can cover a pretty fair cross-section of the
available records by listening to: Alfred Deller (Vanguard, VRS 479), Burl Ives (Decca, DL 5490), Susan
Reed (Elektra, EKL 116), Jean Ritchie (with three versions on Collector Limited Edition, CLE 1201, and West-
minster, WP 6037), Pete Seeger (Folkways, FA 2319),
Stan Wilson (Cavalier, CAV 5505), and Ed McCurdy
(Tradition, TLP 1003).

Nine Pound Hammer

This nine-pound ham-mer— it's a lit-tle too heav-y,— Bud-dy, for my size. Bud-dy, for my size.

Chorus

So, roll on, bud-dy,— Don't you roll— so slow. How can I roll— when the wheels won't go?

Ain't nobody's hammer in this mountain
That rings like mine, that rings like mine.

Well, I went up on the mountain just to see my baby;
And I ain't a-comin' back, Lord, I ain't a-comin' back.

When I'm long gone you can make my tombstone
Out of number nine coal, out of number nine coal.

It's a long way to Hazard; it's a long way to Harlan,
Just to get a little brew, just to get a little brew.*

   * *Hazard and Harlan are Kentucky towns. You may
substitute "booze" for "brew" if you prefer.*

If you're addicted to Bluegrass music (count me in!)
you should go for this one in a big way. It's a long-time
favorite with country blues-style specialists and has been
recorded by many artists, including Merle Travis, The
Monroe Brothers, and Mainer's Mountaineers. A very
similar version to the one shown below was recorded by
Smiley Hobbs in his *Mountain Music Bluegrass Style*
(Folkways, FA 2318) album.

The Jug Of Punch

Moderately

As I was sit-ting with a jug and spoon on
one fine morn in the month of June. A
bird-ie sang on an iv-y bunch And the
song he sang was "The Jug of Punch."

Chorus

Too ra loo ra loo, too ra loo ra loo, too ra
loo ra loo, too ra loo ra loo. A
bird-ie sang on an iv-y bunch and the
song he sang was "The Jug of Punch."

What more diversion can man desire?
Than to warm himself by an alehouse fire;
Upon his knee is a pretty wench,
Aye, and on the table a jug of punch.

*Substitute "A Kerry pippin and the crack and crunch"
for the third line above if you like.*

All ye mortal lords drink your nectar wine
And the quality folks drink their claret fine;
I'll give them all the grapes in the bunch
For a jolly pull at the jug of punch.

Let the doctor come with all his art;
He'll make no impression on my heart.
Even the cripple forgets his hunch
When he's snug outside of a jug of punch.

If I get drunk, well, my money's my own,
And them as don't like me can leave me alone.
I'll tune my fiddle and rosin my bow;
        Aye, and I'll be welcome where'er I go.

And when I'm dead and in my grave
No costly tombstone shall I crave.
Just lay me down in my bed of peat
With a jug of punch at my head and feet.

For my money it's a close race between the Germans and
the Irish as to which people have come up with the best
drinking songs. Without a doubt this one from the Irish
is one of the best. This version combines verses from
Volume 11, Number 3 of *Sing Out* (which came their
way via Francis McPeak and Peggy Seeger) with verses
I have picked up over the past few years. Two good recorded versions are: The Clancy Brothers' *Come Fill
Your Glass With Us* (Tradition, TLP-1032) and A. L.
Lloyd's *English Drinking Songs* (Riverside, RLP 12-
618). Change the last two lines of the chorus each time
to include the last two lines of the verse that has just
been sung.

Hootenanny Granny

FRED HERTZ AND CHARLES GREAN

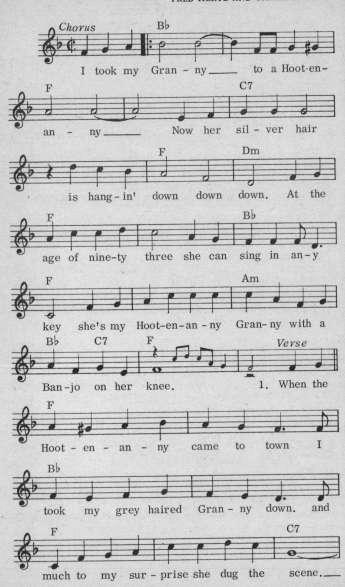

Chorus — I took my Gran - ny ___ to a Hoot-en-an - ny ___ Now her sil - ver hair is hang-in' down down down. At the age of nine-ty three she can sing in an-y key she's my Hoot-en-an - ny Gran-ny with a Ban-jo on her knee.

Verse — 1. When the Hoot - en - an - ny came to town I took my grey haired Gran - ny down. and much to my sur - prise she dug the scene. ___

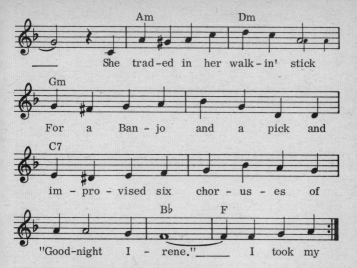

She trad-ed in her walk-in' stick For a Ban-jo and a pick and im-pro-vised six chor-us-es of "Good-night I - rene." I took my

2. Oh she picked the cotton fields in **G**—And then she
     plucked the lemon tree
     She sang the foggy dew from night till dawn
     The Kingston Trio are the rage, but added up
         they're not her age
     For she's the one who knows where all the flowers
         have gone.

3. She helped Michael row the boat ashore—And when
     they hollered out for more
     She sang a verse of blowin' in the wind
     She helped John Henry lay some track—Walked
         along with Reverend Black
     And while the crowd was walkin' out she sang
         "Walk Right In."

4. When the hootenanny finished late, my greyhaired
     granny hopped a freight
     Five hundred miles or more went rollin' by
     We got a card the other day—From the San
         Francisco Bay—
     She's starring at a place they call "The Hungry
         Eye."

On a cold March day in 1964 a bunch of the boys were
making things warmer at a Jimmy Dean Show rehearsal

on 66th Street in New York. In the midst of the normal
confusion of dancers, actors, directors, technicians, props,
and musicians was a small huddle composed of Homer
and Jethro, Cy "Piano Roll Blues" Coben, Charlie
Grean, and a few other on- and off-Broadway hillbillies.
When I mentioned I was putting the finishing touches
on *Hootenanny Tonight* everybody insisted I include
Charlie Grean's name-dropping granny song, which Jim
Lowe had recorded with timely success during the first
big hootenanny boom of the year before. So here it is. We
had the benefit of some of the highest-priced fiddle talent
in the country to give it a real hoedown flavor, as well
as a country-music who's who of singers to pass around
the verses to. But the song comes across with any kind of
motley crew as long as you assemble a crowd and throw
away your inhibitions. Charlies won't mind if you add
verses of your own by laughing at current favorites, singing groups, and situations.

This Train

This train is bound for glo - ry,

This train,__ This train is bound for glo - ry,

This train.__ This train is bound for glo - ry,

Don't ride noth-in' but the right-eous and the ho - ly,

This train is bound for glo - ry, This train.__

This train don't carry no gamblers,
        This train,
This train don't carry no gamblers,
        This train,
This train don't carry no gamblers,
No hypocrites, no midnight ramblers,
This train is bound for glory, this train.

This train is built for speed now, *etc.*
Fastest train you ever did see,
This train is bound for glory, this train.

This train don't cary no liars, *etc.*
No hypocrites and no high flyers,
This train is bound for glory, this train.

This train you don't pay no transportation, *etc.*
No Jim Crow and no discrimination,
This train is bound for glory, this train.

This train don't carry no rustlers, *etc.*
Sidestreet walkers, two-bit hustlers.
This train is bound for glory, this train.

This hootenanny favorite provided the title for Woody
Guthrie's fascinating autobiography, *Bound for Glory*.
The man who wrote "two or three ballads for breakfast
every morning" didn't write this one, but he sure could
pour a lot of life into singing it. You can keep anyone
you want off this train. The verses shown here will give
you an idea of the variety in current circulation.

Early One Morning

This beautiful English song is usually sung in the short form indicated first below. The additional verses help enlarge on the maiden's problem and extend the song to ballad form.

Ear - ly one morn - ing, just as the sun was ris - ing, I heard a maid - en sing - ing in the val - ley be - low. Oh, don't de-ceive___ me. Oh, nev - er leave___ me. How___ can you use___ a ___ poor___ maid-en so?

Oh, gay are the garlands and red are the roses
I culled from the garden to bind on my brow.
Oh, don't deceive me, etc.

Thus sang the maiden, her sorrow bewailing;
Thus sang the poor maid in the valley below.
Oh, don't deceive me, etc.

Long form:

Remember the vows that you made to me truly,
Remember how tenderly you nestled close to me.
Gay is the garland, fresh are the roses
I've culled from the garden, to bind over thee.

Here I now wander alone as I wonder
Why did you leave me to sigh and complain.
I ask of the roses, why should I be forsaken,
Why must I here in sorrow remain?

Through yonder grove by the spring that is running,
There you and I have so merrily played,
Kissing and courting and gently sporting,
Oh, my innocent heart you've betrayed.

How could you slight so pretty a girl who loves you,
A pretty girl who loves you so dearly and warm?
Though love's folly is surely but a fancy,
Still it should prove to me sweeter than your scorn.

Soon you will meet with another pretty maiden,
Some pretty maiden, you'll court her for a while;
Thus ever ranging, turning and changing,
Always seeking for a girl that is new.

(Note: Last verse is the same as above in short version.)

The lack of modesty and the feigned innocence indicated in the verses may provide the answer to the
question: "How could you use a poor maiden so?"

Silver Dagger

Don't sing love songs.___ You'll wake my
moth - er.___ She's sleep-ing here ___
___ right by my side.___
___ And in her right hand,___
___ a sil - ver dag - ger.___
___ She says that I ___
___ can't be your bride.___

All men are false, says my mother;
They'll tell you wicked lovin' lies.
The very next evening they'll court another;
Leave you alone to pine and sigh.

My daddy is a handsome devil.
He's got a chain five miles long.
And on every link a heart does dangle
Of some poor girl he's loved and wronged.

Go court another tender maiden
And hope that she will be your wife,
For I've been warned and I've decided
To sleep alone all of my life.

"Don't Sing Love Songs" or "The Drowsy Sleeper" is an old ballad with many variants, of which this is one of the most popular today. The Carter Family had their own version which replaced the dagger with a small gun. There is an interesting, moody recording of this song by Joan Baez in her Vanguard album (VRS 9078). In longer versions of the ballad the two lovers run off and kill themselves. In the last verse the dying girl says:

"Oh, I can climb the tallest tree, love,
And I can reach the highest nest,
And I can pluck the sweetest rose, love,
But not the heart that I love best."

Hangman, Hangman

This zipper ballad is one of the most exciting of the famous old British ballads. As "The Maid Freed From the Gallows" it is number 95 in Child's ballad collection. The ballad has a long tradition with many variants, but the plot has remained pretty much intact throughout the years—only the sex of the central character and the melody and playing style seem to change very much. This particular version calls for a fast-paced and exciting rhythmic accompaniment. Listen to Huddie Ledbetter's version on *Leadbelly Memorial: Volume IV* (Stinson, SLP 51). For different versions and interpretations hear Jean Ritchie (Collector Limited Edition, CLE 1201), Andrew Rowan Summers (Folkways, FA 2041), and John Jacob Niles (RCA Camden, CAL 219).

Zipper songs and ballads are a boon to us all since they cut down substantially on what we have to remember for performance. You have to learn a basic format for verse, verses, or chorus and then you just zip a new word or a new line into this format. Presto! you have the next verse. This is hopefully as close to instant folk music as we'll ever get. In "Hangman, Hangman" the zipper works like this. First you learn the first three verses. They provide the basic format for the ballad. Then you work the zipper by substituting *Mother* for *Sister* each time it appears. Repeat the three verses, using all of the same words except for this change. After mother has refused to save you from the gallows you zip in brother and father, and keep repeating the process. It would be going a little too far to get uncles and aunts into the act. You may also zip in the relatives in whatever order pleases you most. In any event, you ultimately zip in the sweetheart by whatever name you want and the situation is saved.

Hang-man, hang-man, slack your rope,
Slack it for a-while. I think I see my sis-ter com-in',
Trav-e-lin' man-y a mile, Lord, trav-e-lin' man-y a mile.

Sister, did you bring me silver?
Sister, did you bring me gold?
Did you bring me anything
To keep me from the gallows pole?
Lord, to keep me from the gallows pole?

I've brought you no silver;
I've brought you no gold;
I've come for to see you hangin',
Hangin' from the gallows pole,
Lord, hangin' from the gallows pole.

Now zip in mother

Hangman, hangman, slack your rope,
Slack it for a while.
I think I see my mother comin',
Travelin' many a mile,
Lord, travelin' many a mile.

Mother, did you bring me silver?
Mother, did you bring me gold?
Did you bring me anything
To keep me from the gallows pole?
Lord, to keep me from the gallows pole?

I've brought you no silver;
I've brought you no gold;
I've come for to see you hangin',
Hangin' from the gallows pole,
Lord, hangin' from the gallows pole.

Continue, as above, zipping in brother and father and finally:

Hangman, hangman, slack your rope,
Slack it for a while.
I think I see my sweetheart comin',
Travelin' many a mile,
Lord, travelin' many a mile.

Laurie, did you bring me silver?
Laurie, did you bring me gold?
Did you bring me anything
To keep me from the gallows pole,
Lord, keep me from the gallows pole?

I have brought the silver;
I have brought the gold.
I have brought you everything
To keep you from the gallows pole,
Lord, to keep you from the gallows pole.

Railroad Bill

Railroad Bill was the name picked up by Morris Slater, a Negro outlaw, while robbing freight cars in Alabama and Florida in the 1890's. Law enforcement officers were unable to apprehend the boxcar-bandit for three years, during which his reputation for a charmed life became legendary. Several officers were killed by Slater before he was shot down while munching crackers and cheese in a little country store in Atmore, Alabama. Paul Clayton has recorded this song for Folkways (FA 2110) as has Cisco Houston (FA 2013).

Rail - road Bill, Rail - road Bill, He nev - er worked and he nev - er will. And it's ride, ride, ride, ride.

Railroad Bill, mighty bad man,
Shot all the lamps right off of the stand.
And it's ride, ride, ride.

Railroad Bill, so mean, so bad,
Took everything the poor farmer had.
And it's mean old Railroad Bill.

Railroad Bill, mighty bad,
He shot his maw and beat up his dad.
And it's ride, ride, ride.

Somebody told my lovin' wife,
All about—well, my past life.
It was Railroad Bill.

Railroad Bill led a mighty bad life.
Always hookin' some other man's wife.
That's Railroad Bill.

Railroad Bill, whistlin' a tune,
Shot MacMillan by the light of the moon.
And it's ride, ride, ride.

Four policemen dressed in blue,
Come around the corner two by two,
Lookin' for Railroad Bill.

Everybody told him, he better get back,
Policemen comin' down the railroad track,
Lookin' for Railroad Bill.

Sheriff went up on number five;
He went to get him dead or alive;
So long, Railroad Bill.

Railroad Bill, before he died,
Said he'd build a railroad for the hoboes to ride,
Ride on, Railroad Bill.

The Cat Came Back

Old Mister John-son had trou-bles of his own, He had a yel-low cat Who would-n't leave its home. He tried and he tried to give the cat a-way. He gave it to a man who was go-ing far a-way. But the

Chorus

cat came back, the ver-y next day. The cat came back, They thought he was a gon-er, But the

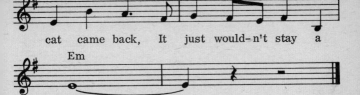

cat came back, It just would-n't stay a

way.

The man around the corner swore he'd kill the cat on
    sight.
He loaded up his shotgun with nails and dynamite.
He waited and he waited for the cat to come around.
Ninety-seven pieces of the man is all they ever found.

He gave it to a man going way out west;
Told him to take it to the one he loved best.
First the train hit the curve; then it jumped the rail.
Not a soul was left behind to tell the gruesome tale.

Away across the ocean they did send the cat at last.
Vessel only out a day and taking water fast.
People all began to pray, the boat began to toss.
A great gust of wind came by and every soul was lost.

On a telegraph wire, sparrows sitting in a bunch.
The cat was feeling hungry; thought he'd like 'em for a
    lunch.
Climbing softly up the pole, and when she reached the
    top,
Put her foot upon the electric wire which tied her in a
    knot.

The cat was a possessor of a family of its own,
With seven little kittens till there was a cyclone;
Blew the houses all apart and tossed the cat around.
The air was full of kittens and not a one was found.

*At present day hoots the following verse is frequently
added to end the song:*

The atom bomb fell just the other day.
The H bomb fell in the very same way.
Russia went—England went—and then the U.S.A.
The human race was finished without a chance to pray.

Just before the turn of the century this comedy song was
composed by Harry S. Miller. It was introduced by Billy

Rice of Harvey's Minstrels with great success and soon became part of our American folk tradition as unknown composers began to add verses here, there, and everywhere. Some of the verses shown here are taken from a composite version collected by Ethel Raim in New York City and published in *Sing Out* in 1959. Sigmund Spaeth, the musicologist, has traced Harry Miller's creation back to an earlier French prototype, "Le Chat de Mère Michel."

Betty And Dupree

Bet - ty told Du - pree: "I want a dia - mond ring."____ ____ Bet - ty told Du - pree: "I want a dia- mond ring."____ Du-pree said: "Oh, yes, Bet - ty, For you I'd do most an- y - thing."____

Dupree said: "Go to sleep. See what tomorrow brings."
Dupree said: "Go to sleep. See what tomorrow brings."
"Sure as the sun comes up, you'll get a diamond ring."

Continued, as above:

Now, Dupree he had a gun, it was a forty-four.
He stuck it in his pocket; went to the jewelry store.

Police they caught Dupree and took him off to jail.
He told 'em send for Betty to come and go his bail.

To the jailhouse Betty went; his face she could not see.
She asked the jailor, "Please, take him this note from
    me."

"They wouldn't let me in to let me see your face.
You know I love you, baby, but I just can't take your
    place."

Dupree he told the judge: "I'm not so brave and bold.
The reason why I did it, I wanted Betty's jelly roll."

The judge he told Dupree: "Jelly roll done ruined you."
"Your honor, set me free, with jelly roll I'm through."

The judge he told Dupree: "I think you quit too late.
You shot a policeman and hangin' is your fate."

Dupree walked into a jewelry store in Atlanta one De-
cember day in 1921 and picked out a diamond ring for
Betty. In attempting to leave the store in a hurry, without paying for the ring, Dupree encountered a policeman
intent on his apprehension. Dupree shot the policeman
with his forty-four. The law eventually caught up with
Dupree in Detroit. He was returned to Atlanta where he
was tried and convicted. He was hanged on September 1,
1922, but not before the balladeers had immortalized him
with this popular blues ballad. "Betty and Dupree" has
been recorded by Josh White (ABC Paramount, ABC
124), Brownie McGee (Folkways, FA 2030), and Paul
Clayton (Folkways, FA 2310).

Omie Wise

Naomi Wise, a nineteen-year-old orphan, loved Jonathan
Lewis. Jonathan loved the beautiful Naomi and promised
to marry her—but that was before he saw he had a chance
to marry Hattie Elliott and move up in society. Naomi
insisted and Jonathan resisted, while Hattie became sus-
picious. Then the unpredictable Mr. Lewis, on the pre-
text of elopement, took Naomi up the river and drowned
her by pulling her skirt up over her head, tying it like a
sack, and throwing her into the water. Jonathan was
caught later with still another girl, Martha, on his lap,
and jailed. Jonathan escaped from jail and by the time
he was found again the whole affair was so dim in everyone's mind he was acquitted of the murder charge. It was
said he finally confessed to the murder on his deathbed.
So goes the account of the murder that took place in
1808 near Asheboro, North Carolina and that has lived
on in the legend, story, and song of "Omie Wise." Good
recordings are available by Paul Clayton (Riverside,
RLP 12-615 and Folkways, FA 2310), Cynthia Gooding
(Elektra, EKL 107), and Ed McCurdy (Riverside, RLP
12-601).

When he came a-courtin'
Fine stories he did tell.
He told her they'd get married
And he would treat her well.

One night he came and told her,
They'd meet at Adams's spring.
He said he'd bring her money
And lots of pretty things.

He didn't bring no money,
He just brought her one thing.
He showed her in his pocket
A golden wedding ring.

He said, "Jump up behind me;
We'll ride a little way.
We'll go to see the preacher
And we'll get married today."

So she jumped up behind him,
And ridin' they did go,
Ridin' up Deep River,
Where the still waters flow.

"Well, Omie, poor Omie,
I'll tell you my mind,
My mind is for to drown you,
And leave you here behind."

"Oh, pity me, oh, pity me,
Oh, pity me," she cried.
"Just let me go a-mournin'
And not become your bride."

He threw her in the river,
Just below the dam.
Then he rode off and left her,
Just like an innocent man.

They found poor Omie's body,
And it was cold as clay.
They knew that John was guilty
And arrested him that day.

"Oh, hang me, oh, hang me,
Oh, hang me," he did cry.
"I drownded little Omie,
And now I wanta die."

Twenty-One Years

The judge says stand up, boy, and dry up your tears, You're sen-tenced to Nash - ville for twen-ty - one years, So dry up your eyes, babe, and say you'll be mine, For twen-ty - one years, babe, is a might - y long time.

I hear the train whistlin', it'll be there on time,
To take me to Nashville to serve out my time;
The steam from the whistle, the smoke from the stack;
I know you'll be true blue until I get back.

Oh, go to the governor and swear by your soul;
If you can't get a pardon, then try for parole.
If I had the governor where he's got me,
Before Tuesday morning the governor'd be free.

Six months have gone by, babe, I wish I was dead;
This dirty old jailhouse has a floor for a bed.
It's raining and hailing and the stars give no light.
Oh, darlin', please tell me why you never write.

I've counted the days, babe, I've counted the nights;
I've counted the footsteps; I've counted the lights;
I've counted the minutes; I've counted the stars;
I've counted a million of these prison bars.

I counted on you, babe, to get me a break.
I guess you forgot, babe, I'm here for your sake.
You know who is guilty; you know it too well;
But I'll rot in this jailhouse before I will tell.

I've prayed to your mother; I've prayed to the stars;
To my heavenly Father through these prison bars.
I've prayed you'd remember and always be mine,
For twenty-one years, Lord, is a mighty long time.

Come on, you young fellows with hearts brave and true,
Don't believe in a woman; you are beat if you do.
Don't trust any woman, no matter what kind,
For twenty-one years, boys, is a mighty long time.

Answer To Twenty-One Years

I (She) wrote him this letter all covered with tears.
This is my (her) answer to "Twenty-one Years."
Oh, please understand, love, when I did not write;
The Master in Heaven knows my heartsick plight.

Six months have gone by, love, the doctor just said.
For six fevered months, love, I've been sick in bed.
My poor hungry heart, love, was in agony.
The doctor had nothing could help what ailed me.

They say you are bitter 'cause I didn't write;
But a brain that's in fever is dark as the night.
So please understand why I didn't write you;
The Lord up in Heaven knows what I've went through.

The judge made you stand there and dry up your tears.
They sent you to Nashville for twenty-one years.
They shackled your arms, love, they shackled your feet;
But they'll never shackle a love that is sweet.

I went to the Governor; got down on my knees;
Said "Oh, Mister Governor, won't you hear my sad
    pleas?"
I asked for your pardon through my blinding tears.
But all I remember was twenty-one years.

As we stood embracing they tore us apart.
But they never can tear you out of my heart.
They shackled your arms, love, they shackled your feet;
But they never can shackle a love that's so sweet.

Though you've been in prison behind all them bars,
When I get my strength back I'll come where you are.
I'll stand by them high walls and cry through my tears;
And I'll wait for you, love, for twenty-one years.

Folk-song collectors (Davis in Virginia and Randolph in
the Ozarks) have found several versions of this old commercial hillbilly song in folk tradition. When I played
around Texas with various country music bands this
popular prison song was frequently requested. If there
was a girl singer around we would follow it up with the
"Answer to Twenty-one Years." It is quite common to
have answer songs for big hillbilly favorites, and quite
a few girl singers got their start by singing answer songs
to current hits.

Four Nights Drunk

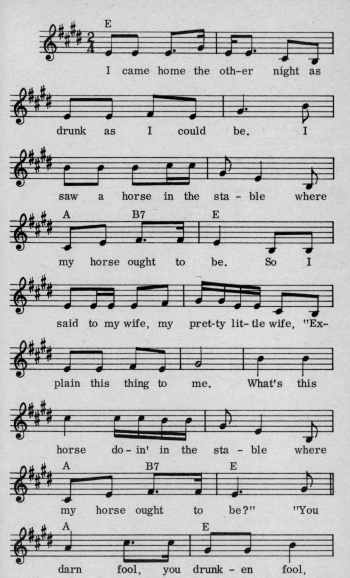

I came home the oth-er night as drunk as I could be. I saw a horse in the sta-ble where my horse ought to be. So I said to my wife, my pret-ty lit-tle wife, "Ex-plain this thing to me. What's this horse do-in' in the sta-ble where my horse ought to be?" "You darn fool, you drunk-en fool,

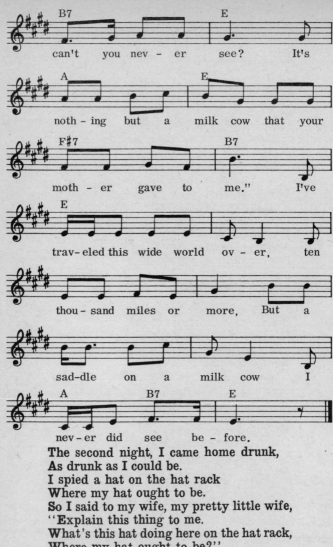

can't you nev-er see? It's noth-ing but a milk cow that your moth-er gave to me." I've trav-eled this wide world ov-er, ten thou-sand miles or more, But a sad-dle on a milk cow I nev-er did see be-fore.

The second night, I came home drunk,
As drunk as I could be.
I spied a hat on the hat rack
Where my hat ought to be.
So I said to my wife, my pretty little wife,
"Explain this thing to me.
What's this hat doing here on the hat rack,
Where my hat ought to be?"
"You blind fool, you drunken old fool,
Can't you never see?
That's nothing but a chamber pot
My granny gave to me."
I've traveled this wide world over,

Ten thousand miles or more,
And a J. B. Stetson chamber pot
I never did see before.

I came home the third night
As drunk as I could be.
I spied some pants upon the chair
Where my pants ought to be.
So I said to my wife, my pretty little wife,
"Explain this thing to me.
What's these pants doing here on the chair
Where my pants ought to be?"
"You blind fool, you drunken old fool,
Can't you never see?
That's nothing but a dishrag
My granny gave to me."
I've traveled this wide world over,
Ten thousand miles or more,
And zippers on a dishrag
I never did see before.

I came home the fourth night
As drunk as I could be.
I spied a head on the pillow
Where my head ought to be.
So I said to my wife, my pretty little wife,
"Explain this thing to me.
What's this head doing on the pillow
Where my head ought to be?"
"You blind fool, you drunken old fool,
Can't you plainly see?
That's nothing but a cabbage head
My granny gave to me."
I've traveled this wide world over,
Ten thousand miles or more,
And a mustache on a cabbage head
I never did see before.

This popular song is several hundred years old and is
still going strong. Many different versions have been collected throughout Europe and America. As "Our Goodman" it is number 274 in the monumental ballad collection of Francis James Child, the famous 19th century
ballad scholar. A German version by Friedrich Wilhelm
Meyer, published in 1790, contained a denouement in
which Our Goodman beats his wife and explains the blows

as caresses her mother sent to her. There might be an idea in that for contemporary re-composers of folk songs. The Meyer ballad passed into oral circulation in Germany, Scandinavia and Hungary. The Limeliters recorded a modern re-write a few years ago and Ed McCurdy may be heard with a more traditional version on his Elektra LP (EKP 108). Other versions have been recorded by Oscar Brand (Audio Fidelity, AFLP 1906) and Sam Hinton (Decca, DL 8108). You don't have to look far for many other recorded versions. For solo work you will probably want to improvise your own falsetto for the wife's lines—otherwise get a partner.

New River Train

I'm rid-ing on that New Riv - er Train._____ I'm rid-ing on that New Riv - er Train._____ Same old train that__ brought me here, Gon - na car - ry me home a - gain._____

Oh, baby, remember what you said;
Oh, baby, remember what you said;
Remember what you said: You would rather see me
  dead
Than ridin' on that New River Train.

Oh, darlin', you can't love one;
Oh, darlin', you can't love one;
You can't love one and have any fun,
Oh, darlin', you can't love one.

Continue, as above

You can't love two—and your little heart be true.

You can't love three—and still love me.

You can't love four—and love me anymore.

You can't love five—and still stay alive.

You can't love six—and not get in a fix.

You can't love seven—if you want to go to heaven.

You can't love eight—'cause you'll make somebody
  wait.

You can't love nine—and keep 'em all in line.

You can't love ten—and stay out of the county pen.

You can't love eleven—you should've stopped at seven.

This counting song for group singing rivals "Roll Me
Over" in popularity and is allowed in many more mixed-
company groups. It's a natural for harmonizing by ear,
and the verses are easy to remember once you learn the
system. (All you have to do is know how to count, and
appropriately zip in the third line for each verse.) A good
many people prefer to make up their own rhymes to fit
the counting scheme, but you're welcome to use mine if
you want to. You can hear it performed on several albums
including *Mountain Music, Bluegrass Style* (Folkways,
FA 2318), The Laurel River Valley Boys (Judson, J
3031), and Alan Mills (Folkways, FP 709).

The Lightning Express

The Light-ning Ex - press from the
sta - tion so grand was_ start - ing
out on its way._
All of the pas - sen - gers that were on
board __ Seemed to be hap - py and
gay._ But one lit - tle
boy_ who sat by him - self was
read - ing a let - ter he had._

stern old con - duc - tor was
start - ing his rounds Tak - ing tick - ets from
ev - 'ry - one there._ .
Fin - al - ly reach-ing the side of the
boy He gruff - ly de - mand - ed his
fare._ _ "I have no
tick - et," the boy then re - plied, "But
I'll pay you back_ some - day."_

You could plain - ly tell by the
"Then I'll put you off at the

tears in his eyes." That the
next stop we make." But he

con - tents of it made him
stopped when he heard the boy

1.
sad._____ The

2.
say:_____

Chorus

"Please, Mis - ter Con - duc -

tor, Don't put me off of this

train._____ The best friend I

have in this world, Sir, Is

wait - ing for me in pain.____

____ Ex - pect - ing to die an - y

mom - ent, Sir, And may not

live thro' the day. I want to reach

home and kiss moth - er good - bye Be -

fore God takes her a - way."____

"My mother was ailing before I left home
And needed a doctor's care.
So I went to the city, employment to seek,
But could not find any work there.
This morning a letter from sister arrived:
'Come home, mother's dying' it did say.
That's why I'm asking for this ride;
I haven't the money to pay."

A girl sitting near was heard to exclaim:
"If you put him off it's a shame."
Taking his hat, a collection she made,
And the boy's fare was paid on the train.
"I'm obliged to you, miss, for your kindness to me."
"You're welcome," she said, "Never fear."
Each time the conductor would pass through the car
The boy's words would ring in his ear: (Chorus)

The title of this version of "The Lightning Express," an old hillbilly heartbreaker, leads you to expect something like "The Wabash Cannonball" or "Fire Ball Mail" instead of a waltz-beat tear-jerker.

The Lincolnshire Poacher

When I was bound ap-pren-tice in fam-ous Lin-coln-shire,___ Full well I served my mas-ter for___ more than sev-en year,___ Till I took up to poach-ing as you shall quick-ly hear: Oh, 'tis my de-light on a shin-ing night In the sea-son of the year!___

As me and my comrade were setting of a snare,
'Twas then we spied the gamekeeper, for him we did not
  care,
For we can wrestle and fight, my boys, and jump o'er
  anywhere.
Oh, 'tis my delight on a shining night
In the season of the year.

As me and my comrade were setting four or five,
And taking on 'em up again we caught a hare alive,
We took the hare alive, my boys, and through the woods
  did steer.
Oh, 'tis my delight on a shining night
In the season of the year.

I threw him on my shoulder, and then we trudged home,
We took him to a neighbor's house and sold him for a
  crown,
We sold him for a crown, my boys, but I did not tell you
  where.
Oh, 'tis my delight on a shining night
In the season of the year.

Success to every gentleman that lives in Lincolnshire,
Success to every poacher that wants to sell a hare,
Bad luck to every gamekeeper that will not sell his deer.
Oh, 'tis my delight on a shining night
In the season of the year.

Throughout Great Britain and Europe large areas of
land were set aside in the 18th century, and as far back
as the Middle Ages, as game preserves for rich lords'
hunting. Thousands of shepherds and farmers were driv-
en off these lands as they were set aside for the privilege
of the few. Severe penalties were established for poachers
—those who hunt on a private game preserve without
permission. "The Lincolnshire Poacher" is a protest song
of sorts from those days, which is still going strong. (So
are the game preserves.) It has been recorded by John
Runge (Stinson, SLP 88) and Richard Dyer-Bennet
(Stinson, SLP 61).

Willie The Weeper

Willie the Weeper is the most famous legendary "hero" of dope addiction. His song has been around, in many versions, for just about as long as "Frankie and Johnnie." Vance Randolph, the well-known collector of Ozark folk songs, remembers hearing it in a Kansas coal-camp in 1908. The Adventure magazine's "Old Songs That Men Have Sung" department received thirty versions in the 1920's with about a hundred different verses, and variations have appeared here and there in many popular song books and on records. Cab Calloway popularized a Broadway adaptation entitled "Minnie the Moocher" in the 1930's which failed to pass the test of time and faded away—while Willie continued to weep.

The two most popular tunes to which the song is sung are both presented here so you can pick the one you like best. You should feel free to depart from either of these melodies to adapt to the natural accents of the verses, in which considerable variation takes place. The chorus in the first tune version is optional. You may wish to omit the chorus entirely or sing it only with the first, last, or an occasional verse, particularly if you decide on a longer version for performance. The song calls for a slow, syncopated, blues-style (or, as Carl Sandburg says, "insinuating") accompaniment.

You may create further adventures for Willie by turning your imagination loose on the contemporary scene, history, or your own friends and surroundings. In the established tradition, Willie dreams of amorous adventures and high living, going places, doing things, and getting rich quick. He hobnobs with kings, sultans, and potentates. His love affairs include women of note from Cleopatra and the Queen of Sheba to movie actresses. He wins millions gambling and lights his pipe with hundred dollar bills. It's high time someone came up with adventures in outer space, scientific explorations, involvement in international intrigue, and affairs with contemporary sex symbols for Willie. I'd hate to think all the action ended for him twenty or thirty years ago.

Did you ev - er hear the sto - ry 'bout Wil - lie the Weep - er?
He had a job as a chim - ney sweep - er. He had the hab - it and he
had it bad.___ Lis - ten while I tell you 'bout the dream he had.___

Chorus

Teet tee dee dee dee.___
(Teet tee dee dee dee.)___
Toot too doo doo doo.___

84

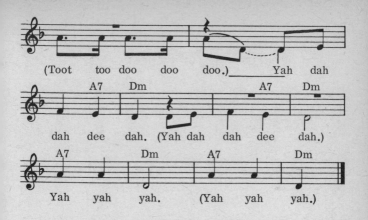

(Toot too doo doo doo.) Yah dah
dah dee dah. (Yah dah dah dee dah.)
Yah yah yah. (Yah yah yah.)

Note: The optional chorus (see headnotes) is arranged here for audience participation. For solo performance omit the responses in third and fourth, seventh and eighth, eleventh and twelfth, and fifteenth and sixteenth measures.

He went to a hop house the other night,
Where the lights were always shining bright.
I guess he smoked a dozen pills or more.
When he woke up he was on a foreign shore.

The Queen of Sheba was the first he met.
She called him her darlin' and her lovin' pet.
She gave him a fancy automobile
With a diamond headlight and a golden wheel.

He landed with a splash in the river Nile,
A-ridin' a sea-goin' crocodile.
He winked at Cleopatra—she said, "Ain't he a sight!
How about a date for next Saturday night?"

He went to Monte Carlo where he played roulette.
He couldn't lose a penny and he won every bet.
He played and he played till the bank went broke.
Then he turned around and took another smoke.

He went off to Turkey by special request.
He stayed seven years as the Sultan's guest.
But when he got in with that harem crew,
What was a poor fellow like Willie to do?

He had a million cattle and he had a million sheep.
He had a million vessels on the ocean deep.
He had a million dollars all in nickles and dimes.
Well—he knew it 'cause he'd counted them a million
　　times.

He landed in New York one evening late.
He asked his sugar to make a late date.
He started to kiss her then he made her pout.
When bing bang bing, the dope gave out.

Now, this is the story of Willie the Weeper.
He's got a job as a chimney sweeper.
Someday a pill too many he will take,
And dreaming he's dead he'll forget to awake.

　Here are some additional verses on Willie's gambling
exploits, more or less in sequence:

He rolled and he smoked about a million pills.
He said, ''These'll cure all my aches and ills.''
It wasn't long until he fell asleep,
And dreamed he was sailing on the ocean deep.

He played draw poker as he left the land,
And won a million dollars on the very first hand.
He played and he played until the crew went broke.
Then he turned around and took another smoke.

He sailed till he came to the isle of Siam.
He rubbed his eyes and said, ''I wonder where I am?''
Played craps with the king and won a million more.
Then he left for Monte Carlo when the king got sore.

He played gin rummy with the King of Iran.
He busted the king with the very first hand.
When he looked around and everybody was broke.
He bought a million dollars worth of hop to smoke.

　Here are some additional miscellaneous verses and a
different ending for you to pick and choose from to de-
velop your own version:

Down in Honolulu Willie fell into a trance
Watching the dusky beauties do a hula-hula dance.
His sweety got in jail, and Willie sure did shout
When he got the news that she had wriggled out.

He bought an ocean liner, all his own,
He loaded it with money and he started to roam.
He said he'd let it go until it wants to stop,
While he counts his money and he smokes his hop.

Then he went to Paris to buy up all the wine.
For a whole carload he paid a measly dime.
He bought a ruby bush and a diamond tree,
And a whole lot of friends to keep him company.

One day while Willie took a quiet smoke,
The ship struck a rock and Willie awoke.
His money was gone and his dream was o'er.
Now he's sweepin' chimneys like he was before.

The first three verses are provided for the second tune version along with a different ending. You will have to borrow verses from the first version to complete the song, and adapt them to the melodic variation.

Did you ev - er hear the stor - y of

Wil - lie the Weep - er?

Wil - lie the Weep - er was a

chim - ney sweep - er.

Had the dope hab - it and he had it bad.

Lis-ten while I tell you 'bout the dream he had.

Around a lay-out table a couple of hop-fiends lay.
Listen and I'll tell you what they had to say:
Tales of the money they were goin' to make
And faro banks they were goin' to break.

Oh, Willie was the biggest dreamer of them all.
Dreamin' that the world was at his beck and call.
When he had smoked a dozen pills or more
He dreamed he was living on a foreign shore.

Insert verses from first version.

Now you've heard the story of Willie the Weeper.
Willie the Weeper was a chimney sweeper.
Went to sleep on his hall-room flop
And dreamed he had a million dollars worth of hop.

Cocaine Lil

"Cocaine Lil" may have been invented by someone to provide a female counterpart to Willie. It may be sung to either tune given for "Willie the Weeper."

Did you ever hear about Cocaine Lil?
She lived in a house on a cocaine hill.
She had a cocaine dog and a cocaine cat.
They fought all night with a cocaine rat.

She had cocaine hair on her cocaine head.
She had a cocaine dress that was poppy red.
But the cocaine blues, they made her sad.
Oh, the cocaine blues they made her feel bad.

She went to a snow party one cold night.
The way she sniffed it was a fright.
There was Hophead Mag with Dopey Slim,
Kankakee Liz and Yen She Jim.

Along in the morning 'bout half-past three,
They were all lit up like a Christmas tree.
Lil went home and started for bed;
She took another sniff and it knocked her dead.

They laid her out in her cocaine clothes.
She wore a snowbird hat with a crimson rose.
And they wrote on her tombstone this refrain:
"She died as she lived, sniffing cocaine."

Knaves Will Be Knaves

I went to the Ale-house as an hon-est wom-an should, And a knave fol-lowed af-ter, as you know knaves would, For Knaves will be Knaves in ev-'ry de-gree, I'll tell you by and by how this Knave served me.

I called for my pot as an honest woman should,
And the knave drank it up, as you know knaves would.
For the knaves will be knaves in every degree;
I'll tell you by and by how this knave served me.

I went to my house as an honest woman should,
And the knave followed after, as you know knaves
    would,
For knaves will be knaves in every degree,
I'll tell you by and by how this knave served me.

I went into my bed as an honest woman should,
And the knave followed suit, as you know knaves would,
For knaves will be knaves in every degree;
I'll tell you by and by how this knave served me.

→

I proved with child as an honest woman should,
And the knave ran away as you know knaves would,
For the knaves will be knaves in every degree,
   And thus I have told you how this knave served me.

"I Went to the Alehouse" is a broadside song from *Wit and Mirth, or Pills to Purge Melancholy* by Thomas D'Urfey. This six-volume collection of songs and poems, "Compleat, Pleasant and Divertive," from the 18th century is one of the monumental collections of its kind and is well known among folk-song enthusiasts—though not generally held in very high esteem because of the large number of non-folk items included. History and song show that knaves haven't changed much since 1719. Oscar Brand's adaptation of the sea-going "A Gob is a Slob" became a hit commercial song with Doris Day when she recorded it as "A Guy is a Guy" almost two-and-a-half centuries after it was written. You should recognize the familiar story immediately in this interesting old version, for which I have provided harmonization only, the rest being entirely as it appeared in D'Urfey's *Pills*.

Reuben Ranzo

Now, Ranzo was no sailor,
Ranzo, boys, Ranzo!
But he shipped on board a whaler,
Ranzo, boys, Ranzo!

And he could not do his duty,
So they took him to the gangway.

For Ranzo was a tailor,
But Ranzo was no sailor.

They gave him nine-and-thirty,
Yes, lashes nine-and-thirty.

The captain being a good man,
Took him into his cabin.

He gave him wine and water.
Rube kissed the captain's daughter.

To fit him for his station;
They taught him navigation.

Though Ranzo was no sailor,
He's first mate of that whaler.

He married the captain's daughter
And sailed across the water.

Oh, Ranzo was a tailor
But now he is a sailor.

And now he's Captain Ranzo.
Hurrah, for Captain Ranzo.

In the days when sailors were sailors, whalers were whalers—no self-respecting able-bodied seaman had any respect for a whaler. Conditions were very bad aboard whalers and it was the opinion of regular sailors that nobody but bums and misfits would sign aboard them. The fact that a good many whalers were recruited from waterfront riffraff amply supported this belief. This popular chantey grew out of these traditional beliefs. When a bungling novice came aboard a ship he was likely to be tagged with the name Reuben which would stick with him until he proved himself. The ingenuity of many creative chanteymen has gone into the invention of these verses which show how fast one of the best Reubens of all time was able to climb the ladder of success aboard a whaler. There is a good recording by A. L. Lloyd and Ewan MacColl (Stinson, SLP 81).

Willow Garden

Way down in a wil - low gar - den Where me and my love___ did meet;___ 'Twas there we sat___ a - court - in', My love dropped off___ to sleep.___ I had with me___ some bur - gun - dy wine___ which my true love did___ not know,___ 'Twas

there I pois - oned that dear lit - tle girl,___ Down___ un - der the banks___ be - low.___

I stabbed her with my dagger,
Which was a bloody knife.
I threw her in the river,
Which was a dreadful sight.
My father often told me
How money would set me free,
If I did murder that dear little girl
Whose name was Rose Connelly.

Now he stands in his cabin door,
Watching with grieving eyes,
Watching his only son
Mounting the scaffold so high.
My race is run beneath the sun
And hell awaits for me,
For I did murder that dear little girl
Whose name was Rose Connelly.

"Rose Connelly" or "The Willow Garden" seems to be an original American murder ballad although it has a story similar to other murder ballads of Irish and English origin. This version was adapted from the singing of George Williams of Portola Valley, California. Among the folk-style singers who have recorded it are Paul Clayton (Riverside, RLP 12-615), The Kossoy Sisters (Tradition, TLP 1018), Herta Marshall (Folkways, FA 2333), and Harry and Jeanie West (Stinson, SLP 36).

Copper Kettle

Get you a cop - per ket - tle,___

___ And get you a cop - per

coil.___ Fill it with new mixed

corn - mash.___ And nev - er

Chorus

more you'll toil.___ You just

lay there by the jun - i - per___

while the fires burn bright.___ Lord, you just

watch them jugs a fil - lin'___ 'Neath the

pale___ moon - light.___

Fill your fire with hickory,
Hickory, ash, and oak.
Don't use no green or rotten wood;
They'll catch you by the smoke.

My daddy he made whiskey.
My granddad, he did, too.
We ain't paid no whiskey tax
Since seventeen ninety-two.

I'd rather drink corn whiskey
Than anything I know.
I'd rather be here on moonshine hill
Than down in the town below.

God bless you, copper kettle;
May you never stop.
Just let me hear that whiskey goin'
Drop, drop, drop.

I don't believe you can find a better moonshine song than
this one, and there are several good ones. Most of the
verses in this version are original with Richard Jaqua, a
Kentuckian who now lives in Woodside, California and
performs mostly around the Bay Area of San Francisco. His version first appeared in *Songs for Swingin'
Housemothers*. Oscar Brand recorded the song in his
Riverside album (RLP 12-630) and it is included in a
Vanguard album by Joan Baez.

Henry Martin

There were__ three bro-thers in mer-ry Scot-land, In__ Scot-land there lived bro-thers three.__ And they did cast lots__ which of them should go,__ should go__ should go__ For to turn rob-ber all on the salt sea.

The lot it fell upon Henry Martin
The youngest of all the three,
That he should turn robber all on the salt sea, salt sea,
    salt sea.
For to maintain his two brothers and he.

He had not been sailing but a long winter's night.
And part of a short winter's day,
When he espi-ed a lofty stout ship, stout ship, stout ship,
Come a-bibing down on him straightway.

"Hello, hello," cried Henry Martin,
"What makes you sail so high?"
"I'm a rich merchant ship bound for fair London Town,
  London Town, London Town,
Will you please for to let me pass by?"

"O no, O no," cried Henry Martin,
"That thing it never can be,
For I have turned robber all on the salt sea, salt sea,
  salt sea,
For to maintain my two brothers and me.

"So lower your topsail and brail up your mizzen,
Bow yourselves under my lee,
Or I shall give you a fast flowing ball, flowing ball,
  flowing ball,
And your dear bodies drown in the salt sea."

With broadside and broadside and at it they went
For fully two hours or three,
Till Henry Martin gave to her the death shot, the death
  shot, the death shot,
Heavily listing to starboard went she.

The rich merchant vessel was wounded full sore,
Straight to the bottom went she,
And Henry Martin sailed away on the sea, salt sea,
  salt sea,
For to maintain his two brothers and he.

Bad news, bad news, to old England came,
Bad news to fair London Town,
There was a rich vessel and she's cast away, cast away,
  cast away,
And all of her merry men drowned.

Here is a contemporary version of the famous traditional
British ballad as it appeared in *Sing Out* in 1962. There
are many different versions current today and the story
line is developed somewhat differently in some. In this
version the pirate sails safely away with his mission
accomplished. In other versions Henry Martin is either

fatally wounded in the encounter or is finally captured and taken to London where he is hanged. Burl Ives (Decca, DL 8080), Ewan MacColl and A. L. Lloyd (Riverside, RLP 12-627) and Dick Wilder (Elektra, EKL 18) are among those folk artists with interesting recordings.

Red Apple Juice

With a banjo, fiddle and guitar you can make this modal mountain-song really sound like it ought to. Let the banjo and fiddle take turns between each verse and use the guitar for a fast-paced, strong rhythm.

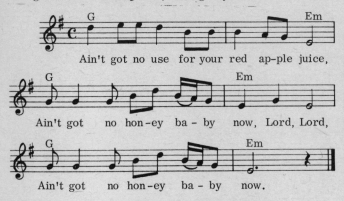

Ain't got no use for your red ap-ple juice,
Ain't got no hon-ey ba - by now, Lord, Lord,
Ain't got no hon-ey ba - by now.

Don't give a care for your red rocking chair;
Ain't got no honey baby now, Lord, Lord,
Ain't got no honey baby now.

Who'll rock your cradle? Who'll sing your songs?
Who'll rock your cradle when I'm gone? Lord, Lord,
Who'll rock your cradle when I'm gone?

I'll rock the cradle; I'll sing the songs;
Don't need no man when you're gone, Lord, Lord,
Don't need no man when you're gone.

It's all I can do; it's all I can say;
Can't get along without you nohow. Lord, Lord,
Can't get along without you nohow.

It's all I can do; it's all I can say.
Sing it to your mama next payday. Lord, Lord,
Sing it to your mama next payday.

Can The Circle Be Unbroken

For I followed close behind her;
Tried to cheer up and be brave;
But my sorrows, I could not hide them,
When they laid her in the grave.

Went back home, Lord, my home was lonesome,
Since my mother she was gone.
All my brothers and sisters crying;
What a home, so sad and lone.

This old gospel favorite promises a return to the status quo and a future with friends and loved ones in the great by and by. It is very much in the old-timey tradition of sentimental songs, religious and otherwise, that have flourished in the southern mountain country for half a century. It is quite popular today with banjo-frailing city billies. You can hear it performed by George Pegram and Walter Parham on a Riverside LP (RLP, 12-650).

The Roving Gambler

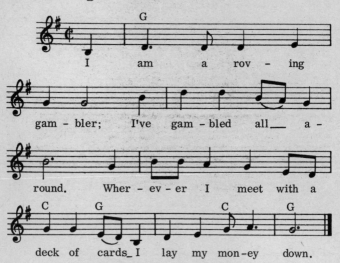

I am a rov - ing gam - bler; I've gam - bled all __ a - round. Wher - ev - er I meet with a deck of cards_ I lay my mon - ey down.

I've gambled in Alaska; I've gambled over in Spain;
I'm on my way to Georgia to knock down my last game.

I had not been in Washington for many more weeks
   than three,
When I fell in love with a pretty little girl and she fell
   in love with me.

She took me in her parlor; she cooled me with her fan;
She whispered soft in her mother's ear: "I love that
   gamblin' man."

"Oh, daughter, my dear daughter, why do you treat me
   so?
How can you leave your dear old mother and with a
   gambler go?"

"Oh, mother, my dear mother, you know I love you
   well;
But the love I have for the gamblin' man no human
   tongue can tell.

"I wouldn't marry a doctor, they're always gone from
   home;
All I want is a gamblin man 'cause he won't leave me
   alone.

"I hear the train a-comin'; she's blowin' 'round the
   curve;
She's a-whistlin' and a-blowin' and a-strainin' every
   nerve.

"Oh, mother, my dear mother, I'll tell you if I can;
If you ever see me coming' back it'll be with a gamblin'
   man."

If you want to extend this song, and you're pretty good
at creating verses, you can make up some around the
other vocations that are distasteful to the gal who has
gone for a gambler. Only a doctor is included here, but
there are many verses in the tradition which cancel out
lawyers, bankers, farmers, preachers, and so on. The
words of the song start out in the first person and subsequently move around as they frequently do in folk
songs. You can recast the words in an impersonal (or personal, if you're a girl) third-person recitation if you
prefer. For more ideas listen to Logan English (Riverside, RLP 12-643), Cisco Houston (Folkways, FA 2346),
Alan Lomax (Tradition, TLP 1029), Ed McCurdy (Elektra, EKL 124), and John Jacob Niles (RCA Camden,
CAL 219).

The Yellow Rose Of Texas

There's a yel - low rose in Tex - as I'm go - ing there to see. No oth - er fel - ler knows her, No - bod - y else but me. She cried so when I left her it like to broke my heart. And if we ev - er meet a - gain We nev - er more will part. She's the

Chorus

sweet - est rose of col - or a

fel - ler ev - er knew. Her
eyes are bright as dia - monds, They
spar - kle like the dew. You may
talk a - bout your dear - est maids and
sing of Ros - a - lie, But the
yel - low rose of Tex - as beats the
belles of Ten - nes - see.

Where the Rio Grande is flowing and stars are shining
bright,
He walked along the river on a quiet summer night.
She said, "If you remember, we parted long ago;
You promised you'd come back and never leave me so."

Oh, I'm going back to find her because I love her so;
We'll sing the songs together we sang so long ago.
I'll play the banjo gaily and sing the songs of yore;
And the yellow rose of Texas will be mine forever more.

Most folk-song enthusiasts aren't very keen about singing along with Mitch. When Mitch Miller was fantastical-

ly successful in getting the masses to sing along with him on this tune in the 1950's, the folk-style singers pretty well committed the song to limbo. Nevertheless, it's not as bad as some people make it out to be, and its widespread popularity makes it a reasonably good folk song for group singing. In any event, here it is—with apologies to everyone. Go on and hoke it up.

Greenback Dollar

I don't want____ your green-back dol - lar.____ I don't want____ ____ your watch and chain.____ All I want____ is you, sweet dar - lin'.____ Won't you take____ ____ me back a - gain.____

Original words by James Leisy. Copyright © 1963 by James Leisy Music, Portola Valley, California. Used by permission.

Once you loved with fond affection;
And your thoughts were just of me.
Now you've left me for another
And you care no more for me.

I don't want your greenback dollar,
And those things you sent to me.
If your conscience bothers you,
Let it be, just let it be.

Oh, there's changes in the ocean;
Yes, there's changes in the sea;
And there's changes in the weather,
But there'll be no change in me.

I don't want your greenback dollar.
You can't buy your conscience free.
I just want your arms around me.
Darlin', please, come back to me.

I have never particularly liked most of the popular versions of this hillbilly standard because the verses are so disjointed and there is rarely a consistent story line. Many versions also end violently with verses like this one:

I don't want your greenback dollar.
I don't want your diamond ring.
All I want is a thirty-eight special.
I'll blow out your dirty brains.

I created this more satisfying version out of lines and ideas from several other songs, including "Fond Affection" and "Go Bring Me Back My Blue-Eyed Boy."

Sir Eglamore And The Dragon

Sir Eg - la - more,_that val - iant knight

Fa, la, lank - y down dil - ly; He

took up his sword_ and went to fight,

Fa, la, lank - y down dil - ly. And

as he rode o'er hill and dale, All

arm - ed with a coat of mail, Fa la

la la la la lank-y down dil - ly.___

There leaped a dragon out of her den,
Fa la lanky down dilly;
And one that had slain God knows how many men,
Fa la lanky down dilly.
But when she saw Sir Eglamore
You should have heard that dragon roar!
Fa la, la la, la la, lanky down dilly.

Continue, as above:

And then the trees began to shake,
While men did tremble and women did quake.

The birds with fright, they all were peeping,
And children everywhere were weeping.

But though the crowd was filled with fear
As they fell to it, they all did cheer,
And to it they went, and they did fight,
A live-long day from morn till night.

The dragon had a horny hide,
That could the sharpest steel abide,
No sword could enter her at all,
But still the knight fought on with gall.

And when the dragon was weary and sore
And tired of sporting with Eglamore,
Then just as yawning she did fall,
He thrust the sword up hilt and all.

Then like a coward she did fly,
Unto her den which was nearby,
And there she lay all night and roared,
So pricking was the knight's good sword.

When all was done to the alehouse he went,
And presently his twopence was spent,
He was so hot with fighting the dragon
That nought could quench his thirst but a flagon.

And now let's pray for the King and the Queen,
And eke in London that may be seen,
As many knights and as many more,
And all as good as Sir Eglamore.

The villagers wanted his sword to be,
A trophy to stand for all to see,
The knight he valued more his health,
And said, "Go get it by yourself."

This may be "the tune chivalry died on" but where I
come from it's a favorite around campfires on dragon-
hunts. My version of this mock-ballad is based on those
found in a host of song books from the 17th century on.
In Playford's *Pleasant Musical Companion,* published
in 1687, this cheerful satire on the stories of the deeds of
the knights is described as "courage crowned with con-
quest: A brief relation how that valiant knight and
heroick champion, Sir Eglamore, bravely fought with,
and manfully slew, a terrible, huge, great, monstrous
dragon. To a pleasant new tune." The last verse, which

I have added to the original, may be omitted by those who are strong for authenticity. *Eke* means all. The phrase, fa la lanky down dilly, provides a good opportunity for audience participation—and that may be the only way you can hold onto your audience.

Johnny Has Gone For A Soldier
(Buttermilk Hill)

This popular love song from the American Revolutionary War is derived from a beautiful old Irish song, ''Shule Aroon.'' You may simplify the chording by omitting the F chord shown in parentheses in the sixth measure and continuing with the A minor chord.

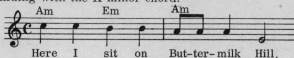

Here I sit on But-ter-milk Hill,

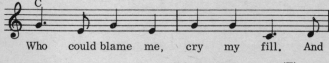

Who could blame me, cry my fill. And

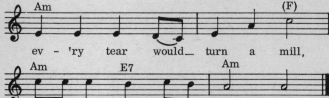

ev-'ry tear would— turn a mill,

John-ny has gone for a sol - dier.

Me, oh my, I love him so;
It broke my heart to see him go;
And only time will heal my woe.
Johnny has gone for a soldier.

I'll sell my flax, I'll sell my wheel;
I'll make my love a sword of steel;
And this in battle he will wield.
Johnny has gone for a soldier.

I'll dye my dress; I'll dye it red;
And through the streets I'll beg for bread
Till he comes back and we are wed.
Johnny has gone for a soldier.

The West Virginny Hills

WORDS BY MARVIN MOORE AND JAMES LEISY

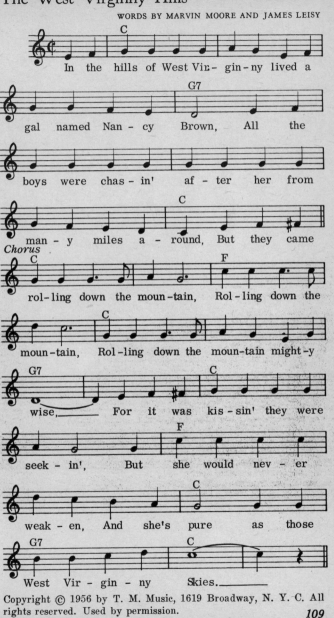

In the hills of West Vir-gin-ny lived a gal named Nan-cy Brown, All the boys were chas-in' af-ter her from man-y miles a-round, But they came

Chorus

rol-ling down the moun-tain, Rol-ling down the moun-tain, Rol-ling down the moun-tain might-y wise,_____ For it was kis-sin' they were seek-in', But she would nev-er weak-en, And she's pure as those West Vir-gin-ny Skies._____

Then there came a fancy cowboy with his chaps and
    with his frills,
And he went to see our Nancy Brown away up in the
    hills.
But he came rolling down the mountain,
Rolling down the mountain,
Rolling down the mountain mighty wise.
He couldn't put his rope around her,
So he left her like he found her,
Just as pure as the West Virginny skies.

Then there came a hot rod driver and his heart was full
    of hope,
As his little midget racer went a-speedin' up the slope.
But he came rolling down the mountain,
Rolling down the mountain,
Rolling down the mountain mighty wise.
Yes, he had his motor racin'
But she put him in his place 'n'
Stayed as pure as the West Virginny skies.

Then there came a city slicker with his hundred dollar
    bills,
And he went to visit Nancy Brown away up in the hills,
And he came rolling down the mountain,
Rolling down the mountain,
Rolling down with Nancy by his side.
And before he knew what hit him,
Matrimony up and bit him,
And now Nancy is his little blushing bride.

"Nancy Brown" or "Rolling Down the Mountain" is an old hillbilly song that has long been popular with hillbilly bands, college students, and back-room piano players. Over the years a good many verses have been created but unfortunately most of them are unprintable. Marvin Moore and I wrote this version for Homer and Jethro, who introduced it as "an old clanker with a new lyric (the words are changed, also). It has a certain nothing to it that will grow on you. However, like most growths it may be removed by proper surgery." It's in their *Bare-foot Ballads* album (RCA Victor, LPM 1412).

Strolling Through Norfolk

While strol-ling thro' Nor-folk one day on a spree, I spied a bold pack-et with sail fly-ing free. She was broad in the count-er and bluff in the bow, So I took in my sail and cried: "Way e-nough now!"

Chorus

Ov-er the o-cean I've sailed mer-ri-ly: A trim-mer young pack-et I nev-er did see.

I hailed her in English; she answered in play,
So yard-arm to yard-arm we went on our way.
We hauled up our courses and soon left the rest;
And when we dropped anchor she'd shown me the best.

We went to a tavern where soon we did moor
At a table for two right beside the dance floor.
Oh, we sat there and drank till I thought I would drown
And I couldn't keep up with her round after round.

I promised her all if she only would go,
Like treasures and trinkets from the islands, you know,
And I said she could have all my money to spend . . .
And she saw that it was when the evening did end.

I picked up a couple of verses and the chorus to this song
when I was in the Navy during World War II. In the
years that followed I added verses from here and there
until I ultimately discovered it was a variant of a fore-
castle ballad, "As I Went A-Walking Down Ratcliffe
Highway"—or vice versa, though that is much less likely.
Ratcliffe Highway, near Limehouse Reach and the East
India Docks in the port of London, caters to sailors with
its taverns, dance halls, and tailor shops. It is quite pos-
sible the song originated there in the 19th century, as is
suggested by William Doerflinger in *Shantymen and
Shantyboys*.

The Farmer Who Went Out For Beer

There was a jol - ly old farm - er man who start - ed to go out for beer,_____ He start - ed to go out for beer,_____ _____ He start - ed to go out for beer, af - ter Hup sa, sa, tra la, la, la, He start - ed to go out for beer._____

Translation by James Leisy. Copyright © 1963 by James Leisy Music. Used by permission.

A student then came to his sweet young wife
When the old man had gone out for beer,
When the old man had gone out for beer,
The old man had gone out for beer, out for
Hup sa, sa, tra la, la, la,
The old man had gone out for beer.

Continue, as above:

Her rosy red lips the young student kissed
And tenderly patted her cheek,
While the old man was out after beer,
While the old man was out after beer, after, *etc.*

But the farmer was hiding behind the door
And saw all that happened within,
While they thought he was out after beer,
They thought he was out after beer, after, *etc.*

The farmer he took a dim view of this
And booted them both out the door.
And then he went out after beer,
The farmer went out after beer, after, *etc.*

Now, farmers should profit from this advice:
When out after beer take your wife.
Take your wife when you're out after beer,
Take your wife when you go out for beer, out for, *etc.*

The moral for students is plain to see:
Behind the door take a look
When the old man is out after beer,
When you think that he's out after beer, after, *etc.*

When exchange students became the fashion on American campuses after World War II it was inevitable that
some of their folkways rub off on American students. This
Scandinavian song has been popular with students
throughout Europe for a good many years. Several trans-
lations and versions are now widely known and sung on
American campuses. This version is my translation from
the singing of Norwegian students at Stanford, Berkeley,
and U. C. L. A. It's a grand song for mixing beer-drink-
ing with robust singing.

The Old Maid's Song

Chorus

Come a lands-man a pins-man a tin-ker or a tai-lor,___
Fid-dler or a danc-er a plough-boy or a sai-lor,___
gent-le-man a poor man a fool or a wit-ty, Don't you
let me die an old___ maid, but take me out of pi-ty.___

Oh, I had a sister Sally, was younger than I am,
She had so many sweethearts, she had to deny them;
As for my own part I never had many,
If you all knew my heart, I'd be thankful for any.

(Chorus)

Oh, I had a sister Susan, was ugly and misshapen,
Before she was sixteen years old she was taken,
Before she was eighteen, a son and a daughter,
Here am I six and forty and nary an offer.

(Chorus)

Oh, I never will be scolding, I never will be jealous,
My husband shall have money to go to the alehouse,
While he's there a-spending, well I'll be home a-saving,
And I'll leave it to the world if I am worth having.

(Chorus)

Here's an old courting song with a new angle that has
been very popular, particularly with girl performers, at
twentieth century folk-song revival hootenannies. The
song has been around well over a hundred years in both
English and American versions. This version is based on
the singing of Peggy Seeger in her Folkways album,
Folksongs of Courting and Complaint (FA, 2049), as
is was transcribed for the tenth-anniversary issue of
Sing Out in 1961.

The Foolish Frog

Pete Seeger has never failed to amuse an audience with
his singing monologue about the foolish frog. Here it is,
as he wrote it, in its entirety. If you have a knack for
story-telling and acting, it's well worth working up for
a hoot. You may hear him perform it on his Folkways
record, *Birds, Beats, Bugs, and Bigger Fishes*.

It all started this way. (Whistling is heard. A sassy little
tune.)

There was once a farmer, walking down the road, whistling a tune to himself. He said, "Dog-gone, I wish I had
some words to that song. But all I've got is the melody."

Just then he came to a little bridge, and he leaned on
the railing, looking down at the brook. There was a big
old bullfrog, hopping from bank to bank. (Sound effects.)

Well, the bullfrog looked up, and saw the farmer, and decided to show off. He took an extra special big hop. Z-z-z-z-ztt! He landed, splash! in the water, and got himself all wet. The farmer laughed and laughed and started singing:

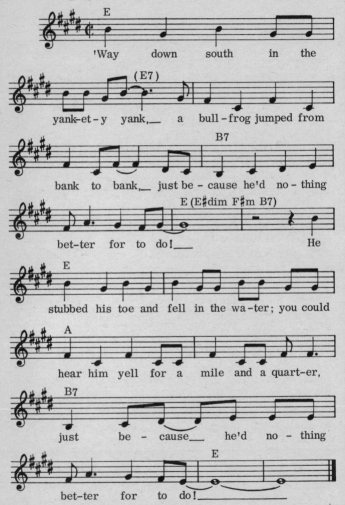

'Way down south in the yank-et-y yank,— a bull-frog jumped from bank to bank,— just be-cause he'd no-thing bet-ter for to do!— He stubbed his toe and fell in the wa-ter; you could hear him yell for a mile and a quart-er, just be-cause— he'd no-thing bet-ter for to do!—

Now, the farmer went walking down the road, feeling mighty proud of himself for making up a song. He went down to the corner store, bought himself some groceries, and a pair of work gloves, and a plug of chewing tobacco, and said:

"Oh, before I go, I have to sing you my new song."

"Go on home," says the storekeeper. "I'm busy here. See all these customers."

"I won't pay you my money unless you let me sing my song!"

"Well, sing it and get it over with," says the storekeeper.

The farmer started singing, and the man in the store cried out, "That's a wo-o-onderful song. Gather 'round everybody, we'll have a party!" And he passed around the free Coca-Colas and the free soda crackers, and everybody was stamping on the floor.

Meanwhile, all the wives and children back home were sitting down to supper, and—where's father? The mothers said, "Children, you better run down to the corner store and fetch your old man. He's probably down there wasting his time as usual."

So all the children run down the road. They run inside the corner store. You know, they heard all that music, they forgot all about coming home. The children started singing. (Tune is repeated in a high voice.) And they were passing around the free Cola-Colas and. . . .

Now, in every farmhouse it was the same situation. The mothers said to themselves, "This has gone far enough. Supper's getting cold. 'Spect us to work all day and nobody show up?" They reached over on the stove and grabbed some heavy frying pans and start down the road with a mad look in their eyes. Somebody's going to get beaned. Well, they get near, and hear all that pretty music, and they forget all about being mad. They drop the frying pans in the gutter, walk in the store, and the mothers start singing! "Way down south in the yankety-yank, a bullfrog jumped from bank to bank. . . ." And they were passing around the free Coca-Colas and the free soda crackers, and everybody was stamping on the floor!

Meanwhile, out in the barns, all the cows started talking. "Where is everybody? We're supposed to be milked, and it's getting mighty uncomfortable!" So the cows left their stalls; they wobbled out of the barn and down the road right into the corner store. And the cows started singing: "Moo, moo, moo, moo. Moo, moo, moo, moo. Moo-moo, moo-moo, moo-moo, moo-moo, moooooo." And the cow tails were swishing out the windows, and they were stamping on the floor, and drinking the free Coca-Colas and eating the free soda. . . .

Out in the barnyard all the chickens said, "Where is everybody? We're supposed to be fed and we're getting hungry." So the chickens hopped over the fence, hopped down the road, hopped into the store, and the chickens started: (Chicken imitation.) And the chickens were stamping on the floor and drinking the free Coca-C. . . .

Meanwhile all the barns started talking to each other. "We feel mighty lonely," they said, "without any cows, or any chickens. I guess we'll have to go find them." So the barns picked themselves off their foundations, and galumphed down the road, and s-q-u-e-e-z-e-d themselves into that corner store, believe it or not. Did you ever hear a rusty hinge on a barn door? That's the way the barns sang: "Eeeeee, eeeeee, errrrrrrrrrrrrr."

Out in the fields, all the grass says: "Where is everybody? The cows are supposed to come and eat us. I guess we'll have to go find them." And the grass picked itself up and swished off down the road, and swished right into the store, and the grass started singing: "Sh-sh-sh-sh-sh-sh-sh. Sh-sh-sh-sh-sh-sh-sh. Sh-sh-sh-sh-sh-sh-sh-sh-sh-shhhh."

Of course, when the grass was gone, the fields were gone, so the brook didn't have any banks to flow between. It said, "I've got to go someplace." The brook bubbled down the road. It bubbled right up into the corner store, and the brook started, "Bububdublbldububldubedl-bub!"

The brook was bubbling up and down the stairway! The grass was growing out the chimney! Feathers flying through the air! Cows' tails swishing out the windows! Everybody stamping on the floor and drinking the free Coca-Colas and eating the free soda crackers!

Meanwhile, there's the bullfrog in mid-air!

He looks down. There's nothing underneath him. He looks over, and there's no bank to land on. He says, "Where am I?" And he starts hopping down the road. Hop! Hop! Hop! Hop!

"Hey, what's that racket down at the corner store?" says the frog.

"Why . . . they're singing! They're singing about ME!" And he was so proud he puffed himself up with pride.

And he puffed,
      and he puffed,
            and he puffed,
                  and he

P O O M ! ! !

He exploded. Cows, barns, chickens, farmers, the whole corner store went up in the air, and everybody floated down and landed right where they were supposed to have been all the time. They all sat down eating supper again, feeling kind of foolish for themselves.

Next day they went out to find the frog. They looked high, they looked low. Coca-Cola bottles and soda crackers in all directions. But no frog. So all there is left of the frog is the song. We might as well sing 'er once again.

(Sing tune through, and then whistle it, for conclusion.)

The Suicide Song

Oh, come with me to the kitch-en,— To the kitch-en,— to the kitch-en.— Oh, come with me to the kitch-en,— And there a date with death we both will keep. Turn on the gas in the ov-en,— in the ov-en,— in the ov-en.— Turn on the gas in the ov-en,— And it will gent-ly lull us both to sleep. Lis-ten to the his-sing sounds, Lis-ten to the his-sing sounds. They're

Words by Pat Blanke and James Leisy, music by Alice Haw-thorne. Copyright © 1961 by James Leisy Music. Used by per-mission.

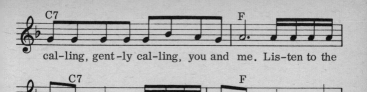

cal-ling, gent-ly cal-ling, you and me. Lis-ten to the

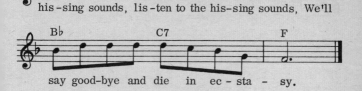

his-sing sounds, lis-ten to the his-sing sounds, We'll

say good-bye and die in ec-sta-sy.

We'll close the doors and the windows,
And the windows, and the windows,
We'll close the doors and the windows,
And sniff each whiff until we drift away.
We'll leave a note on the table,
On the table, on the table,
We'll leave a note on the table:
''Milkman, don't leave us any milk today.'' *(Chorus)*

Pat Blanke of New York and I wrote these words to the
tune of ''Listen to the Mockingbird'' one gloomy Sun-
day afternoon. It had a certain appeal in the high days
of sick humor and I performed it occasionally and included it in the sick-song section of *Songs for Swingin'
Housemothers.* I never really thought much of it, despite
audience enthusiasm, until I began hearing it back from
others in remoté corners of the country. Pat and I were
pleased to become a poor folks' Tom Lehrer—particularly
when we heard he'd bought the book.

Whistle, Daughter, Whistle

Moth-er, I would mar-ry, yes, I would be a bride, and I would have a young man for-ev-er at my side. For if I had a young man, oh how hap-py I would be, for I am tired and oh, so wea-ry of my sin-gu-la-ri-ty.

Whistle, daughter, whistle, and you shall have a cow.
I cannot whistle, mother, I guess I don't know how.
But if I had a young man, oh, how happy I would be,
For I am tired and so weary of my propriety.

Whistle, daughter, whistle, and you shall have a sheep,
I cannot whistle mother, I can only weep.
But if I had a young man, oh, how happy I would be,
For I am tired and oh, so weary of my virginity.

Whistle, daughter, whistle, and you shall have a man.
I cannot whistle, mother, . . . (whistles)
You impudent little daughter, what makes you whistle
    now?
I'd rather whistle for a man than for a sheep or cow.

Here is a contemporary version of a very old song as it
appeared in *Sing Out*. There are many different versions
of the song that have been popular throughout Europe
and America. There is a German, Flemish, and French
round from the 15th or 16th century in which a nun or
monk is tempted to dance by similar offers. For contemporary versions listen to A. L. Lloyd (Riverside, RLP
12-614), Jean Murai (Stinson, SLP 75), Peggy Seeger
(Folkways, FA 2049), and Ellen Stekert (Stinson, SLP
49).

I Know Where I'm Goin'

I'll give up silk stockings,
And shoes of bright green leather,
Combs to buckle my hair,
And rings for every finger.

Feather beds are soft,
And painted rooms are bonnie;
But I would trade them all
For my handsome, winsome Johnny.

Some say he's a bad one,
But I say he is bonnie.
Fairest of them all
Is my handsome, winsome Johnny.

Repeat first verse.

I think this is one of the most effective songs a girl can
sing. It comes from Ireland and probably is related to the
Gypsy Laddie family of songs which includes ''The Gypsy Rover,'' ''The Wraggle Taggle Gypsies,'' and ''Gypsy
Davey.'' The D chord in the last measure of this harmonization provides a natural transition into each suc-
ceeding verse and allows an ending which leaves the
listener suspended—wondering whether he has heard
the whole story. This interesting effect will add to the
expressiveness of your performance but if it jars you
too much you can resolve the problem and the song by
ending it conventionally with a G chord. Recordings include The Weavers (Decca, DL 5825), Kathleen Ferrier
(London, 5411), Patrick Galvin (Riverside, RLP 12-
608), and Burl Ives (Columbia, CL 6109).

Corena

"Corena" or "Corinna" was a frequently featured song on the hillbilly radio programs I listened to in the 1930's. It remained popular when I was playing in the 1940's and may still be heard frequently today. It certainly has become what might be called a standard of Tin Pan Valley. Alan Lomax found many versions in wide circulation among Negro and hillbilly singers under these and other titles, including "Alberta" and "Roberta."

Cor - en - a, Co - ren - a,____
____ where you been so long?____
Cor - en - a, Co - ren a,____
____ where you been so long?____
____ I ain't had no lov - in'____
Since you been gone.____

Corena, Corena, where did you stay last night?
Corena, Corena, where did you stay last night?
Come in this morning, sun shining bright? ➡

I love Corena, tell the world I do.
I love Corena, tell the world I do.
Just a little more lovin'; let your love be true.

I met Corena, far across the sea.
I met Corena, far across the sea.
Won't write me no letter; she don't care for me.

Corena, Corena, oh, fare you well,
Corena, Corena, oh, fare you well,
If I don't meet you in heaven, I'll see you in hell.

Everyday Gossip

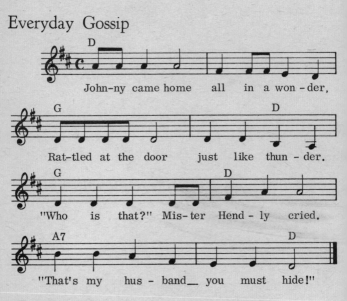

John-ny came home all in a won-der,
Rat-tled at the door just like thun-der.
"Who is that?" Mis-ter Hend-ly cried.
"That's my hus-band__ you must hide!"

She held the door while old man Hendly,
Shakin' and a-jerkin' went up the chimney.
John came in and looked all around
But not a soul could be found.

John set down by the fireside weepin',
Then up the chimney he got to peepin'.
There he spied that wretched soul
Sittin' a-straddle on the pot rack pole.

John built on a rousing fire
Just to suit his own desire.
His wife cried out with a free good will:
"Don't do that or the man you'll kill."

John reached up and down he fetched him.
Like a raccoon dog he catched him.
Blacked his eyes, and then he done better,
Throwed him out right on his setter.

His wife crawled up under the bed.
He drug her out by the hair of her head.
Said "When I'm gone remember this!"
Then he kicked her where the kickin's best.

Oh, the law came down and John went up.
He didn't have the chance of a yellow pup,
They put him on to the old chain gang
For beatin' his wife, that poor little thing.

When John got out she took him to court.
There she got him for non-support.
John didn't worry—John didn't cry,
But when he got close he punched her in the eye.

So back he went to the old town jail.
His wife come down and run his bail.
Pretty soon now he'll be loose.
I could tell you more—but it ain't no use.

"Will the Weaver" has been a popular ballad in English and American folk traditions since at least the 18th century. Commercial hillbilly singers recorded it frequently in the 1920's and 1930's under various titles and with different versions. Charlie Parker and Mack Woolbright recorded "Will the Weaver" for Columbia (15694) in 1927 (released in 1931), David McCarn made "Everyday Dirt" for Victor (40274) in 1930, and in 1935 Bill Carlisle came up with a song entitled "Jumpin' and Jerkin' Blues" which was released on several labels, including Vocalion (02984) and Conqueror (8789). The song is also known under the titles "Chimney Pole" or "Chimney Hole." The version shown here was current around Texas in the 1930's.

The Fox

The fox went out on a chil-ly night,
Prayed for the moon to give him light, For he'd
man-y a mile to go that night be-
fore he reached the town - o, the
town - o, the town - o, He'd
man-y a mile to go that night Before he reached the town - o.

He ran till he came to a great big pen
Where the ducks and the geese were put therein,
"A couple of you will grease my chin
Before I leave this town-o,

This town-o, this town-o,
A couple of you will grease my chin
Before I leave this town-o."

130

Similarly:

He grabbed the gray goose by the neck,
Throwed a duck across his back;
He didn't mind their quack, quack, quack,
And their legs all dangling down-o *(etc.)*

The old mother Flipper-Flopper jumped out of bed,
Out of the window she cocked her head,
Crying, "John, John, the gray goose is gone,
And the fox is on the town-o" *(etc.)*

Then John, he went to the top of the hill,
Blowed his horn both loud and shrill;
The fox, he said, "I better flee with my kill
Or they'll soon be on my trail-o" *(etc.)*

He ran till he came to his cozy den;
There were the little ones eight, nine, ten.
They said, "Daddy, better go back again,
For it must be a mighty fine town-o" *(etc.)*

Then the fox and his wife without any strife
Cut up the goose with a fork and knife;
They never had such a supper in their life,
And the little ones chewed on the bones-o *(etc.)*

This has been such a hootenanny favorite over the past
few years it is about to become as reliable as "On Top of
Old Smoky," "Down in the Valley," and "Goodnight,
Irene" for group singing. The versions are pretty standardized and a good many people know the words by
memory. In any event, it's a good warm-up song and
lots of people get a kick out of rolling those classic words
around on their tongues.

There are many, many recordings available, including
those by Stan Wilson (Verve, MG V-2019), Woody
Guthrie (Folkways, FC 7015), Josef and Miranda
Marais (Decca, DL 5268), Ellen Stekert (Folkways, FA
2354), Harry Belafonte (RCA Victor, LPM 1022), and
Pete Seeger (Folkways, FA 2321).

In The Pines

True love, true love, don't lie to me, Tell me where did you sleep last night._____ I slept in the pines where the sun nev-er shines And I shiv-ered when the cold wind_ blowed._____ To the pines, to the pines, where the sun · nev-er shines and you shiv-er when the cold wind_ blows._____

Chorus

You slighted me once; you slighted me twice;
But you'll never slight me no more.
You caused me to weep; you caused me to mourn;
You caused me to leave my home.   *(Chorus)*

Them long steel rails with short crossties
Gonna carry me away from home.
That lonesome track gonna take me back
Where a man can call his soul his own.   *(Chorus)*

The longest train I ever saw
Was on the Georgia line.
The engine passed at five o'clock;
The caboose done passed at nine.   *(Chorus)*

The longest day I ever saw,
Ever since I started to roam,
Was the day I left my own true love,
The day I left my home.   *(Chorus)*

Now, don't you hear those mournin' doves
Flyin' from pine to pine,
Mournin' for their own true love
Just like I mourn for mine.   *(Chorus)*

You'll have to look very far to find a blues more unusual
than this moody one from the southern mountain country. It is known by several titles and there is considerable
variation among the different versions. Even the har-
monizations vary a great deal, so if you don't like mine
try one of your own. You can study two styles with Paul
Clayton (Folkways, FA 2110) and the Kossoy Sisters
(Tradition, TLP 1018). Then hear Leadbelly's "Black
Girl" in *Leadbelly Memorial: Volume III* (Stinson, SLP
48) or *Rock Island Line* (*Leadbelly Legacy: Volume 2*)
(Folkways, FA 2014).

The Wagoner's Lad

From the same family of songs which has given us "On Top of Old Smoky," "The Cuckoo," and many others, comes one of the most popular Anglo-American love ballads. Several good recordings include Peggy Seeger (Folkways, FA 2049), Pete Seeger (Folkways, FA 2320), Buell H. Kazee (Folkways, FS 3810) and The Kossoy Sisters (Tradition, TLP 1018).

Oh, I am a poor girl, my for-tune's been bad, For a long time I've court-ed the wag-o-ner's lad. He court-ed me fair-ly by night and by day, But now he has load-ed and is go-ing a-way.

I loved him so dearly, I thought he loved me,
But now he is leaving, he wants to be free.
"Go put up your horses and feed them some hay,
Come sit down beside me for as long as you can stay."

"My horses ain't hungry, they won't eat your hay,
So fare you well darling, I'm going away."
"It's raining, it's hailing, the moon gives no light,
Your horses can't travel that dark road tonight."

"My horses are harnessed, my whip's in my hand,
So fare you well, darling, my horses won't stand."
"Oh, must you then leave me to see you no more,
To stay here a-weeping on the wild river shore?"

"Your parents don't like me, they say I'm too poor,
They say I ain't worthy to enter your door.
Yes, your parents are against me and you are the same,
Dig deep in your heart, dear, and blot out my name."

"I know they don't like you, but what do you care?
For I am your true love and I am your dear,
And I would have consented your bride for to be,
But my parents aren't willing for you to have me."

"I came to your city to stay for awhile,
I left my dear parents, went many a mile.
But you want a freeholder and I have no land.
Now, that is your true love as I understand."

"I earn my own living, my money's my own,
And if they don't like me, they can leave me alone.
So early this morning I did then arise
To cross the wild river with tears in my eyes.

"I'm going to Georgia and there I will roam,
And then I'll make Georgia to be my new home.
On top yonder mountain I'll look back this way,
With tears in my eyes my last goodbye I will say."

"But when you get to Georgia you'll cry there I fear,
When you think of the loved one you left waiting here."
"I'll ride on to Georgia and write you my mind,
For I mean to marry and leave you behind."

And that is the fortune of poor womankind,
Forever controlled and forever confined,
Controlled by their parents till they are made wives,
Then slaves to their husbands the rest of their lives.

Toorali

The en-list-ed men ride in a mot-or launch,___ The Cap-tain he rides in a barge;___ It won't go a damned___ bit fast-er,___ But it gives the old bug-ger a charge.___ *Chorus* Sing-ing, Too - ra - li, too - ra - li, too-ra-li.___ Too - ra - li, too - ra - li ay.___

Too - ra - li, too - ra - li,
too - ra - li._____ Too - ra - li,
too - ra - li ay._____

The enlisted men eat in the wardroom,
But the Captain won't eat with a gob,
It ain't that he eats any better,
He don't want us to see he's a slob.

The enlisted men sleep in their hammocks,
But the captain he sleeps in a bed,
He don't sleep a damned bit better,
But he's twenty feet nearer the head.

The armed services have extensive folk-song traditions.
"Toorali" comes from World War II and is based on
earlier ancestors. You'll have no problem getting audience participation on the choruses.

The Water Is Wide

This song has a long and strong Anglo-American tradition and many variants exist. For three different versions listen to Isla Cameron (Tradition, TLP 1001), John Runge (Riverside, RLP 12-814), and Pete Seeger (Folkways, FA 2321).

Oh, the wa - ter is wide, I cannot cross ov - er,____ And neith - er
have I wings to____ fly.____
____ But give me a boat that
will car - ry two,____ And both shall
row, my love and_ I.____ .

A ship there is and it sails the sea.
It's loaded deep as deep can be.
But not so deep as this love I am in,
I know not how I sink or swim.

I put my finger into the bush
To pluck a rose of fairest kind.
The thorns they pierced me at a touch,
And so I left that rose behind.

I leaned my back against an oak,
Thinking that it was a trusty tree.
But first it bended and then it broke,
As did my false lord to me.

Oh, love is sweet and love is fair,
Fresh as the dew when first it is new,
But love grows old and waxeth cold
And fades away like morning dew.

Oh, the water is wide, I cannot cross over.
And neither have I wings to fly.
But give me a boat that will carry two,
And both shall row, my love and I.

The Four Maries

Last night there were four Mar - ies. To - night there'll be but three. There was Mar - y Beat - on and Mar - y Seat - on, And Mar - y Car - mich - ael and me.

Oh, often have I dressed my queen
And put on her braw silk gown;
But all the thanks I've got tonight
Is to be hanged in Edinburgh town.

Full often have I dressed my queen;
Put gold upon her hair;
But I have got for my reward
The gallows to be my share.

They'll tie a kerchief around my eyes
That I may not see to dee;
And they'll never tell my father or mother,
But that I'm across the sea.

Last night there were four Maries,
Tonight there'll be but three;
There was Mary Beaton and Mary Seaton,
And Mary Carmichael and me.

Ballad scholars have criticized the quality of this popular ballad because it tells the story in the first person.
One of the standards by which they judged ballads (at
least in the past) was the detached and objective presenta-
tion of the story by the balladeer. This short version is
the best-known in this country. The longer versions fill
in the details of a lengendary scandal in the court of
Mary, Queen of Scots. There are so many Mary's in the
song and the historical scene that it is difficult to keep
them all straight. This is understandable since the folk
tradition seems to have hopelessly confused the situation
anyhow. The queen did have four ladies-in-waiting who
were popularly known as "the four Maries" and her reign
was noted for court scandals and rumors of scandal.
Historians, however, have not as yet turned up a real
Mary Hamilton who was associated with Queen Mary in
the 16th century. They have located a Mary Hamilton
who was a Scottish maid-of-honor in Peter the Great's
court and was beheaded for infanticide (the crime in this
ballad) in 1719. Since fact and fiction are frequently in-
termingled in folklore, nobody really seems to mind.
Among the artists who have recorded this ballad are
John Jacob Niles (RCA Camden, CAL 330), Cynthia
Gooding (Elektra, EKL 131), Hermes Nye (Folkways,
FA 2305), and Jeannie Robertson (Riverside, RLP 12-
633).

Abilene

Ab – i – lene,__ Ab – i – lene,__
pret – ti – er town I nev – er seen.__
Folks there don't treat you mean_ in Ab – i –
lene, my Ab – i – lene.

I sit alone most every night
Watching the trains as they pull out of sight.
Don't I wish they'd carry me back to Abilene, my
    Abilene.

Old empty boxcar standing all alone;
Wheels all rusted; it ain't no home;
But it will take me home to Abilene, my Abilene.

Been to Chicago, Frisco, too,
New York City, just won't do.
So I'll be headin' back to Abilene, my Abilene.

Saw New York City in the drizzlin' rain,
Headlights flickerin' on my window pane;
Made me so lonesome for my Abilene, old Abilene.

Crowded city—ain't nothin' free—
Nothin' in this town for me.
So I'll be headin' home to Abilene, my Abilene.

In 1963 George Hamilton IV came up with a pop and
country-music hit version of this popular old traditional

blues (RCA Victor, 8184). My version differs a little and includes several traditional verses that were left out of the pop version. You can add to the effectiveness of your performance by whistling the chorus to a soft thumb-strum accompaniment at the beginning and end of the song. Another good recording of "Abilene" to listen to for ideas was produced by Anita Kerr and Chet Atkins in Nashville in 1963, *Folk Song Festival Featuring Walter Forbes* (RCA Victor, LPM-2670). For an earlier recording listen to Bob Gibson (Riverside, RLP 12-806). The verses are sung to the same tune as the chorus with slight modifications in the melody to accommodate extra words. The chorus may be repeated between verses at your option.

Where Are You Goin', My Good Old Man?

Oh,__ where are you go - in', my good old man?__ Where are you go - in', my hon - ey lov - ey lamb? Where are you go - in', my good old man?__ The best old man in the world.__

Spoken: **Goin' to the saloon where I always go.**

Oh, why are you goin' there, my good old man?
Why are you goin' there, my honey lovey lamb?
Oh, why are you goin' there, my good old man,
The best old man in the world?
Spoken: **To get drunk like I always do.**

Continue, as above:

Won't you go after supper, my good old man?
Spoken: **All right, if you'll quit jawin' and fix it.**

Oh, what'll you have for supper, my good old man?
Spoken: **A bushel full of eggs like I always have.**

How do you want 'em cooked, my good old man?

Spoken: **Fry 'em in vinegar like you always do.**

Ain't you afraid they'll kill you, my good old man?
Spoken: **I don't care if they do.**

Where shall I bury you, my good old man?
Spoken: **In the chimney corner where you always do.**
Ain't you afraid of sniffin' ashes, my good old man?
Spoken: **I don't care if I do.**

Why do you want to be buried there, my good old
man?
Spoken: **So I can ha'nt you.**

A ha'nt can't ha'nt a ha'nt, my good old man.
A ha'nt can't ha'nt a ha'nt, my honey lovey lamb.
A ha'nt can't ha'nt a ha'nt, my good old man;
Meanest old devil in the world.

Songs like "Buffalo Boy," "There's a Hole in My Bucket" and this one provide great material for a boy and a girl to team up for a comedy routine. Ad libbing or rehearsed patter and horseplay between the verses is customary. You may also want to work out some personalized verses of your own. One of the verses in my version grew out of an early-morning incident with my sleepy-headed wife: half-awake and out of butter she anointed my eggs with vinegar instead of the cooking oil substitute she thought she was using. Listen to Jean Ritchie and Oscar Brand (Elektra, EKL 22) for performance ideas.

Foolish Questions

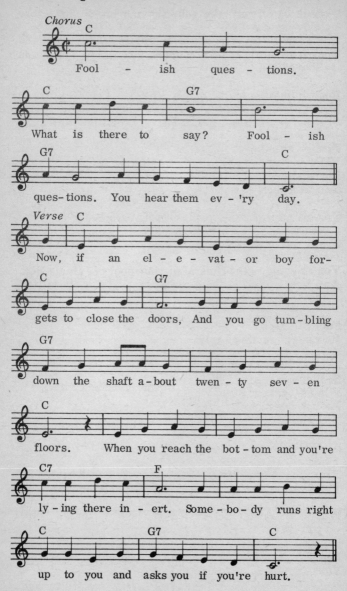

Chorus

Fool - ish ques - tions.

What is there to say? Fool - ish

ques - tions. You hear them ev - 'ry day.

Verse

Now, if an el - e - vat - or boy for-

gets to close the doors, And you go tum - bling

down the shaft a - bout twen - ty sev - en

floors. When you reach the bot - tom and you're

ly - ing there in - ert. Some - bo - dy runs right

up to you and asks you if you're hurt.

I'll bet you've seen those fellows who will hang around
   the place;
They'll watch you take your shaving brush and lather
   up your face;
And as you give your razor a preliminary wave,
They'll stand right there and ask you: "Are you gonna
   shave?"

Foolish questions.
Your answer is, I hope:
Spoken: No, I'm not gonna shave. I just love the taste
   of soap!
Foolish questions.
What is there to say?
Foolish questions.
You hear them every day.

There's a busybody woman who will meet you on your
   way.
She'll ask you where you're going and she'll listen
   while you say,
You're going to the funeral of your poor old Uncle Ned.
And sure as life she'll say to you: "My dear, is Ned
   dead?"

Foolish questions.
You might as well reply:
Spoken: No, he thought he'd have the funeral first—
   then later on he'll die!
Foolish questions.
What is there to say?
Foolish questions.
You hear them every day.

And when you're soundly sleeping in the early morning
   hours,
Dreaming of a pretty girl in a garden full of flowers;
The phone rings at your bedside—it's enough to turn
   your hair—
When half asleep you answer and they ask you: "Are
   you there?"

Foolish questions.
Your answer is, of course:

→

Spoken: **No, this is a recording and you're talking to my horse!**
Foolish questions.
What is there to say?
Foolish questions.
You hear them every day!

This too true commentary on typical reactions of our fellow men (present company is always excluded, of course) was one of the favorite comedy songs in the clubs I worked in Texas in the 1940's. It had been around for years and there were many different versions with no end of humorous situations to exploit. I ran across an old song book from the 1890's in the Cleveland Public Library that had a whole set of situations apropos to those times. The mad, mad, mad Gateway Trio have a hard-driving calypso-beat version in their album (Capitol, T 1868) and Stan Wilson has a rollicking talking version in his *Stan Wilson Goes to College* album (Fantasy, 3336). It calls for a lively, cornball rendition and is particularly effective with a group taking turns on the verses. The questions at the end of each verse are usually spoken rather than sung.

Tell Old Bill
(This Morning, This Evening, So Soon)

Tell old Bill when he comes home this morn-ing, Tell old Bill when he comes home this eve-ning, Tell old Bill when he comes home to leave them down-town gals a-lone, This morn-ing, this eve-ning, so soon.

Old Sal was baking bread, this morning,
Old Sal was baking bread, this evening,
Old Sal was baking bread,
When she found out her Bill was dead,
This morning, this evening, so soon.

She said, "Oh, no, it can't be so," *etc.*
My Bill left here about an hour ago."

She said, "Oh, no, this can't be," *etc.*
"They killed my Bill in the third degree."

Well, they brought Bill home in a hurry-up wagon, *etc.*
Poor dead Bill, how his toes were draggin'.

In talented hands this blues-style ballad has provided the
material for a show-stopping performance at a good many
hootenannies. Bob Gibson has recorded it for Riverside
(RLP 12-806), and Sam Hinton for Decca (DL 8108).

My Cross-Eyed Girl

Oh, she's done and gone a-
way, kicked the buck-et yes-ter-day, My
cross-eyed girl that lives up on the
hill.____ She took strich-i-nine and
died, now I hope she's sat-is-
fied For she done the whole darn
thing a-gainst my will.____

She said goodbye to me as she sat upon my knee.
She said she'd meet me on that golden shore.
But I took it as a joke; didn't think she'd really croak;
For she never died so suddenly before.

We suspected her to die by the color of her eye,
And our efforts to revive her were in vain.
She looked up at me and died, then turned up her nose
    and sighed,
Then raised up and smiled and sneezed and died again.

Oh, she must have had a hunch that she'd leave our
    jolly bunch,
For she had her lawyer name me in her will.
She left me an old rag doll and a broken parasol
And a little old log cabin on the hill.

Now that she has gone to rest I'll fulfill her last request
And plant a bunch of onions by her grave,
So that when I'm passing by I can pucker up and cry
For the dog-gone things they fairly make me rave.

Long, long before Homer and Jethro came along to keep
audiences in stitches at Ryman Auditorium, home of the
Grand Old Opry in Nashville, this kind of bucolic humor
was popular in the hills and the backwoods country. I
learned this particular song (probably a parody of ''The
Little Old Log Cabin in the Lane'') from Tillman Hall,
the well-known folk-dance authority who has directed
dancing for the Lawrence Welk and Art Linkletter television shows. Tillman is now Dr. Hall of the University
of Southern California, but there was a time when he was
just a country boy from Tennessee. He learned the guitar
by ear and imitation, like a good many others, and kept
a ballad book in which he wrote the words down to his
favorite songs. He had this high-spirited bit of foolish-
ness near the front of his book, but he didn't have to look
at the words to refresh his memory at all when he first
played it for me. He is frequently requested to play it
during his travels throughout the United States and Can-
ada each year with his dance group, The Westchester
Lariats.

Beautiful, Beautiful Brown Eyes

Wil - lie, oh Wil - lie, I love you,_____ Love you with all my heart,_____ To - mor - row we might have been mar - ried_____ But lick - er has kept us a - part._____

Chorus

Beau - ti - ful, beau - ti - ful brown eyes,_____ Beau - ti - ful, beau - ti - ful brown eyes,_____

Beau - ti - ful, beau - ti - ful brown eyes,_____ I'll nev - er love blue eyes a - gain._____

Seven long years I've been married,
I wish I was single again,
A woman never knows of her troubles
Until she has married a man.

Down to the barroom he staggered,
Staggered and fell at the door,
The last words that he ever uttered,
"I'll never get drunk any more."

It's always easy to get an audience to sing along with
you on the choruses of this old hillbilly favorite.

Who's Gonna Shoe Your Pretty Little Foot?

Who's gon-na shoe your pret-ty lit-tle foot? Who's gon-na glove your hand? Who's gon-na kiss your red rub-y lips? Who's gon-na be your man? Who's gon-na be your man? Who's gon na be your man? Who's gon-na kiss your red rub-y lips? Who's gon-na be your man?

Papa's gonna shoe my pretty little foot,
Mama's gonna glove my hand.
Sister's gonna kiss my red ruby lips,
I don't need no man,
I don't need no man,
I don't need no man.
Sister's gonna kiss my red ruby lips,
I don't need no man.

The longest train I ever did see
Was a hundred coaches long.
The only woman I ever did love
Was on that train and gone,
Was on that train and gone,
Was on that train and gone.
The only woman I ever did love
Was on that train and gone.

A few centuries back the British were singing about
"The Lass of Roch Royal" like this:

O who will shoe my bonny foot?
Or who will glove my hand?
Or who will bind my middle jimp
With the broad lily band.

The lass was worried about who was going to look after
her while "love Gregor" was many a mile away. During the next thirty or forty verses, depending on the
strength and resources of both singer and audience, the
lass would go looking for Gregor, find his home and get
turned away by his "false" mother, and die in a ship-
wreck on her broken-hearted way back home. When
Gregor got wind of what had happened he went after his
Anny but was unable to catch up until he saw her with
his young son in her arms "baith tossed aboon the tide."
After he paused to "wrang his hands" he "catched her
by the yellow hair an drew her to the strand, but cauld
an stiff was every limb before he reached the land."
Singers today have cut out all of these details and
dropped the ballad form entirely. Listen to Milt Okun
and Ellen Stekert (Riverside, RLP 12-634), Alfred Deller (Vanguard, VRS 1001), Herta Marshall (Folkways,
FA 2333), and Shep Ginandes (Elektra, EKL 7).

Cryderville Jail

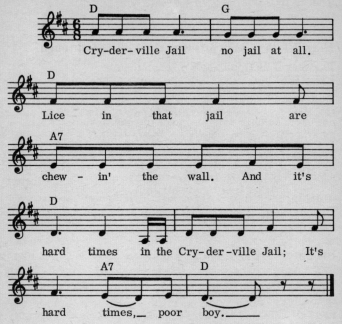

Cry-der-ville Jail   no jail at all.

Lice   in   that   jail   are

chew - in'   the   wall.   And   it's

hard   times   in the Cry-der-ville Jail;   It's

hard   times,__ poor   boy.____

There's a big bull ring in the middle of the floor.
A damned old jailor to close the door.
Well, it's hard times in the Cryderville Jail.
It's hard times, poor boy

Got beds that are made of old rotten rugs.
You sleep on the beds and you're covered with bugs.
Well, it's hard times in the Cryderville Jail.
It's hard times, poor boy.

I wrote to my mother to send me a knife
'Cause the lice and the chinches were threatening my
    life.

Well, it's hard times in the Cryderville Jail.
It's hard times, poor boy.

Continue, as above:

Here's to the lawyer that comes to your cell
And swears he will clear you in spite of all hell.

He'll take all your money before he will rest.
Then tell you "plead guilty, I think that it's best."

You go to the judge and he reads you the law,
Damndest old judge that you ever saw.

The jury you get's a hell of a crew.
They'll look a poor prisoner through and through.

The sheriff he thinks he's a real big shot.
I'm tellin' you, boys, he's the worst of the lot.

Your pockets he'll pick and your clothes he will sell;
Get drunk on the money, now damn it to hell.

Cryderville jail may be "no jail at all" considering what jails might be, but in terms of what jails actually are it appears to be right in step. A federal survey of the nation's 14,000 lock-ups in 1950, condemned most of them as unfit for human habitation. Reform movements over the last two hundred years have improved federal and state prisons considerably, but city and county jails have not changed much. In 1960 the Kilpatrick Committee of the California Legislature found examples in cities like San Francisco that were "dark, dingy, and filthy" with "dried vomit and excrement on the floor." As many as seven idle lousy men were crowded into cells only forty-two feet square, without mattresses, blankets or working toilets. The investigators were unable to determine whether the food there was meant to be served or was garbage. With this background it is not difficult to interpret the bitterness in the words of this song. The tune calls for a hard-driving two beats to the measure. Dave Guard made a spirited recording with his Whiskey Hill Singers for Capitol, and Sam Eskin recorded it for Cook Laboratories (1020).

Little Maggie

This traditional song from the southern mountain country is a great favorite witth banjo-banging citybillies also. For a real, unaffected performance listen to Obray Ramsey's rendition in *Banjo Songs of the Southern Mountains* (Riverside, RLP 12-610). You'll hear quite different versions from The Kingston Trio (Capitol, T996) and Tom Paley (of the New Lost City Ramblers)

Well, yon-der stands lit-tle Mag-gie,___ With a
rum glass in___ her hand, And she's
drink-in' down her trou-bles___ And she's
fool-in' some oth - er man.

Tell me how can I ever stand it,
Just to see those two blue eyes.
They're shining like a diamond,
Like a diamond in the sky.

Sometimes I have a nickel,
Sometimes I have a dime.
And it's sometimes I have ten dollars,
Just to buy little Maggie some wine.

Pretty flowers were made for blooming,
Pretty stars were meant to shine.
Pretty girls were made for boys to love,
And Little Maggie was made for mine.

The first time I seen Little Maggie,
She was starin' straight at me
With a forty-five strapped 'round her shoulder
And a banjo on her knee.

Now, she's goin' down to the station
With a suitcase in her hand.
She's goin' away for to leave me.
She's bound for a distant land.

Fair Ellender

Oh, fath - er, oh, fath - er, come rid - dle to me, Come rid - dle it all___ as one;___ ___ And tell me wheth - er to mar - ry fair El - len, or bring the Brown girl___ home.___

"The Brown girl, she has house and land;
Fair Ellender, she has none;
And there I charge you with a blessing
To bring the Brown girl home."

He got on his horse and he rode and he rode,
He rode till he come to her home;
And no one so ready as Fair Ellen herself,
To rise and welcome him in.

"What news have you brought unto me Lord Thomas,
What news have you brought unto me?"
"I've come to ask you to my wedding,
A sorrowful wedding to be."

"Oh, mother, oh, mother, would you go or stay?"
"Fair child, do as you please.
But I'm afraid if you go you'll never return
To see your dear mother any more."

She turned around all dressed in white,
Her sisters dressed in green;
And every town that they rode through,
They took her to be some queen.

They rode and they rode till they come to the hall,
She pulled on the bell and it rang;
And no one so ready as Lord Thomas himself,
To rise and bid her in.

Then taking her by her lily-white hand,
And leading her through the hall;
Saying, "Fifty gay ladies are here today,
But here is the flower of all."

The Brown girl, she was standing by,
With knives ground keen and sharp;
Between the long ribs and the short
She pierced Fair Ellender's heart.

Lord Thomas, he was standing by,
With knife ground keen and sharp;
Between the long ribs and the short
He pierced his own bride's heart.

Then placing the handle against the wall;
The point against his breast;
Saying, "This is the ending of three true lovers,
God sends them all to rest.

"Oh, father, oh father, go dig my grave,
Go dig it wide and deep;
And place Fair Ellender in my arms,
And the Brown girl at my feet."

This is Mike Seeger's version of the famous British ballad, number 73 in the collection made by Francis J. Child. You may hear him sing it to his own autoharp accompaniment in *The Folk Music of the Newport Folk Festival*, Volume 1 (Folkways, FA 2431). Ewan MacColl has recorded a traditional Scottish version which is in his Folkways album, *Child Ballads* (FG 3509) and his *Classic Scots Ballads* (Tradition, TLP 1015). This transcription is from *Sing Out*.

He's Got The Whole World In His Hands

This popular, simple, repetitive spiritual is particularly suitable for group singing. The zipper structure and the fact that most people know the words anyhow, make it easy for everyone to join in. To stretch out a performance you can repeat the chorus as often as you want to.

He's got the whole world— in His hands, He's got the whole world— in His hands, He's got the whole world— in His hands, He's got the whole world in His hands.—

He's got the little bitty babies in His hands,
He's got the little bitty babies in His hands,
He's got the little bitty babies in His hands,
He's got the whole world in His hands.

He's got you and me, brother, in His hands,
He's got you and me, sister, in His hands,
He's got you and me, brother, in His hands,
He's got the whole world in His hands.

He's got the gamblin' man in His hands,
He's got the gamblin' man in His hands,

He's got the gamblin' man in His hands,
He's got the whole world in His hands.

For additional verses you may zip in: drinkin' man,
worldly sinners, cheaters and the liars, two-bit hustlers,
rich and the poor, meek and the humble, and others of
your own invention.

Let My Little Light Shine

This lit-tle light of mine,____

I'm gon-na let it shine,____

This lit-tle light of mine,____

I'm gon-na let it shine,

This lit-tle light of mine,____

I'm gon-na let it shine,____ ev-'ry

day, ev-'ry day, ev-'ry

day, ev-'ry day,____ gon-na

let my lit-tle light shine.____ On

Mon-day he gave me the gift___ of love. On
Tues-day peace came from a-bove.___ On
Wednes-day told me to have more faith. On
Thurs-day gave me a lit-tle more grace.___ On
Fri-day told me to watch and pray. On
Sat-ur-day told me just what to say.___ On
Sun-day gave me pow-er di-vine___ just to
let my lit-tle light shine.

No hootenanny veteran needs an introduction to this popular gospel song. For some real variety in performance listen to The Gateway Singers (Decca, DL 867), the Howard University Choir (RCA Victor, LM 2166), and Harry and Jeanie West (Folkways, FA 2357).

Heaven Is So High

Heav-en is so high, You can't get ov-er it, So low, you can't get un-der it, So wide you can't get a - round it; you must come in at the door. You might as well just make up your mind, You must come in at the door, Broth-er, soon-er or lat-er you're bound to find, You must come in at the door.

There's only one path that takes you there,
It leads right up to the door;
It's narrow and straight, but it's free from care,
You must come in at the door.

If you get there before I do,
You must come in at the door,
Don't worry or wait, I'm coming, too,
You must come in at the door.

You'll find it's always open wide,
You must come in at the door;
So, brother, don't stop till you're inside;
You must come in at the door.

I've heard this old hand-clappin' gospel song performed a
lot of different ways, including calypso style. Use a toe-
tapping tempo with everyone in the act, and it will swing
if you don't go too fast. For two quite different performances listen to Bob Gibson (Riverside, RLP 12-816)
and The Percentie Brothers (Art, ALP 8).

We Shall Not Be Moved

We shall not, We shall not be moved;
We shall not, We shall not be moved, Just like a
tree that's plant-ed by the wa - ter,
We shall not be moved.

We're fighting for our freedom,
We shall not be moved; *etc.*

We're waiting for our dinner . . .

We're fighting for our children . . .

An old southern hymn was adopted by union singers in the thirties and has been closely associated with protest groups during the twentieth century folk-song revival ever since. It was a favorite of the folksingers of Greenwich Village when they demonstrated against an ordinance preventing them from holding hoots in Washington Square; the freedom riders and other demonstrators in the South; ban-the-bomb protesters; and other groups who have demonstrated against various political and social ideas and activities. It has also served a good many non-political activities in camps, churches and schools. Verses are sung to the same tune as the chorus and are usually made up out of the subject matter of a particu-

lar event. Some examples follow (insert your own choice
for the word *someone*) :

> (Someone) is a stinker,
> We shall not be moved;
> (Someone) is a stinker,
> We shall not be moved.
> Just like a tree that's planted by the water,
> We shall not be moved.
>
> (Someone) is a stinker,
> He should be removed;
> (Someone) is a stinker,
> He should be removed.
> Just like a fly that's sticking in the butter,
> He should be removed.

We Shall Overcome

We shall ov - er - come,___
We shall ov - er - come,___
We shall ov - er - come some -
day.___ Oh,___
down in my heart I do be-
lieve We shall ov - er -
come some - day.___

We will build a new world,
We will build a new world,
We will build a new world some day.
Oh, deep in my heart, I do believe
We will build a new world some day.

Continue, as above:

I will overcome.

I would be like Him.

I will wear a crown.

The truth shall make us free.

The Lord will see us through.

We'll walk hand in hand.

Love will conquer all.

Here is the majestic hymn that has become the theme song of civil rights action groups. *Will* or *shall* are used interchangeably in the title lines according to the preference of the group. Verses are frequently created to fit specific situations—and from these creations a good many live on. Some of the more standard verses are shown below. Singing groups frequently make up substitutions for the lines ''Deep in my heart, I do believe'' to add interest and variation in the repetition of the verses. You may wish to use these substitute lines to add variation to your singing:

> If in my heart, I do not yield.
> Deep in my soul, I will not yield.

In 1963 Vanguard chose this song to issue Joan Baez's first single record (35023).

In conjunction with the reproduction of WE SHALL OVERCOME:
Royalties derived from this composition are being contributed to The Freedom Movement under the trusteeship of the writers.

WE SHALL OVERCOME

New words and music arranged by Zilphia Horton, Frank Hamilton, Guy Carawan and Pete Seeger.

Let Me Fly

Way down yon-der in the mid-dle of the field, An-gel work-in' at the char-iot wheel. Not so par-tic-u-lar 'bout work-in' at the wheel, But I just want-a see how the char-iot feels.

Chorus

Now, let me fly,____ Now, let me fly____ ____ Now, let me fly____ in-to Mount Zi - on, Lord, Lord.____

I got a mother in the Promised Land,
Ain't gonna stop till I shake her hand.
Not so particular 'bout shakin' her hand,

But I just wanna go up in the Promised Land.
Meet that hypocrite on the street,

First thing he'll do is to show his teeth.
Next thing he'll do is to tell a lie,
And the best thing to do is to pass him by.

Gospel songs and spirituals are always popular at hoots, particularly for group singing. Here's a real rouser with a great sense of humor. Erik Darling has recorded it for Elektra (EKL 154).

All The Good Times

There's a haunting, nostalgic quality to this old country song and a universal message that touches home. Once you let this tune get under your skin it stays with you like "Goodnight, Irene" and "Beautiful, Beautiful Brown Eyes." For a country version look up Bill Clifton on Blue Ridge Records. The verses are sung to the same tune as the chorus.

All the good times _ are past _ and gone. All the good times _ are o'er. _ All the good times _ are past _ and gone. Dar - lin', don't weep _ no more. _

I wish to the Lord I'd never been born,
Or had died when I was young;
And never had seen your sparkling blue eyes
Or heard your flattering tongue.

Oh, don't you see that distant train
A-comin' round the bend.
It'll take me away from this old town;
Never to return again.

Oh, don't you see that lonesome dove
That flies from pine to pine.
He's mourning for his own true love
Just like I mourn for mine.

All My Trials

Usually sung in a spiritual-lullaby style, if you can call it that, this very popular song apparently originated with a Baptist hymn that was current in the South after the Civil War and traveled through the folk tradition of the Bahamas before it was found by the twentieth century folk-song revivalists. Listen to the versions by Cynthia Gooding (Elektra, EKL 107) and Joan Baez (Vanguard, VRS 9078).

The river of Jordan is mighty cold.
It chills the body but not the soul.
All my trials, Lord, soon be over.

I've got a little book with pages three,
And every page spells liberty.
All my trials, Lord, soon be over. *(Chorus)*

If religion was a thing that money could buy,
The rich would live and the poor would die.
All my trials, Lord, soon be over.

There is a tree in paradise
The Christians call the tree of life.
All my trials, Lord, soon be over.

There's a little white dove a-flyin' in the blue;
Gonna show what the power of love can do.
All my trials, Lord, soon be over. *(Chorus)*

Eggs And Marrowbone

Want to get rid of your man? This song will tell you one way *not* to do it. This is another song from British folk tradition that has great popularity in the United States. Listen to Richard Dyer-Bennet's version on his Decca album (DLP 5046).

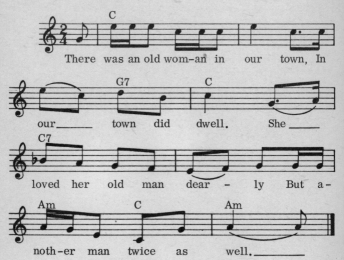

There was an old wom–an in our town, In our town did dwell. She loved her old man dear – ly But a–noth–er man twice as well.

She went down to the doctor
To see what she could find,
To see what she could find, sir,
To make her old man blind.

Eggs, eggs, and marrowbone,
Feed them to him all,
That will make him so gol-dern blind
That he can't see you at all.

She fed him eggs and marrowbone,
Fed them to him all;
That did make him so gol-dern blind
That he couldn't see her at all.

"Now that I am old and blind,
And tired of my life,
I will go and drown myself,
And that will end my strife."

"To drown yourself, to drown yourself,
Now that would be a sin,
So I will go down to the water's edge
And kindly push you in."

The old woman took a running jump
For to push the old man in,
The old man he stepped to one side
And the old woman she fell in.

She cried for help, screamed for help,
Loudly she did bawl.
The old man said, "I'm so gol-dern blind
I can't see you at all."

She swam along, she swam along,
Till she came to the river's brim,
The old man got a great, long pole
And pushed her further in.

Now the old woman is dead and gone,
And the Devil's got her soul.
Wasn't she a blamed old fool
That she did not grab that pole?

Eggs, eggs and marrowbone
Won't make your old man blind,
So if you want to do him in,
You must sneak up from behind.

East Virginia

There are several melodies associated with this popular hillbilly song. Banjo players tend to prefer the one I have used here. The melody used for "Greenback Dollar" in this book is also frequently used. You may wish to try them both and then do some switching according to personal preference. There are several recordings worth listening to, including: Logan English (Folkways, FA 2136), Buell H. Kazee (Folkways, FS 3810), Pete Seeger (Folkways, FA 2003), Pete Steele (Folkways, FS 3828), and Harry and Jeanie West (Stinson, SLP 74).

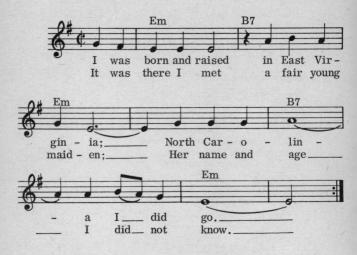

I was born and raised in East Vir-
It was there I met a fair young

gin - ia;_____ North Car - o - lin -
maid - en;_____ Her name and age_____

- a I ___ did go._____
_____ I did__ not know._____

Well, her hair was dark of color,
And her cheeks were rosy red;
On her breast she wore white lilies
Where I longed to lay my head.

I'd rather be in some dark holler,
Where the sun refuses to shine,
Than for you to be another man's darlin',
And to know you'd never be mine.

For when I sleep I'm dreaming of you.
When I'm awake I have no rest.
Minutes seem to me like hours
With aches and pains all through my breast.

In my heart you are my darlin',
At my door you're welcome in.
By my gate I'll always greet you.
For you're the girl I've tried to win.

Johnny, I Hardly Knew You

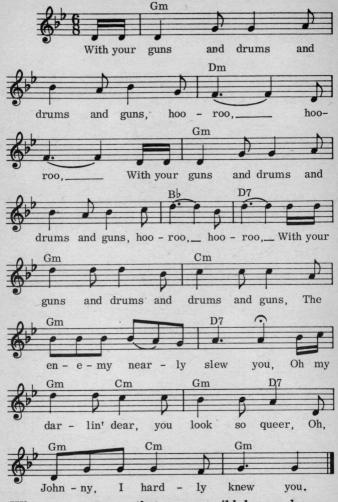

With your guns and drums and drums and guns, hoo-roo, ___ hoo-roo, ___ With your guns and drums and drums and guns, hoo-roo, ___ hoo-roo, ___ With your guns and drums and drums and guns, The en-e-my near-ly slew you, Oh my dar-lin' dear, you look so queer, Oh, John-ny, I hard-ly knew you.

Where are your eyes that were so mild, hooroo, hooroo,
Where are your eyes that were so mild, hooro, hooroo,
Where are your eyes that were so mild
When my heart you first beguiled;
Oh, why did you run from me and the child?
Johnny, I hardly knew you.

Continue, as above:

Where are your legs that used to run, *etc.*
When first you went to carry a gun?
Indeed your dancing days are done.
Oh, Johnny, I hardly knew you.

You haven't an arm you haven't a leg, *etc.*
You're a hopeless shell of a man with a peg.
And you'll have to be put with a bowl to beg.
Oh, Johnny, I hardly knew you.

It's glad I am to see you home, *etc.*
My darlin', you're so pale and wan.
So low in flesh, so high in bone . . .
Oh, Johnny, I hardly knew you.

They're rollin' out the drums again, *etc.*
But they'll never take my sons again,
No, they'll never take my sons again,
Johnny, I'm swearin' to you.

This anti-war version of "When Johnny Comes Marching Home" came from Ireland and was introduced originally to American audiences by Betty Sanders. The last verse was added by Les Pine. By the 1960's it had become a great favorite with folk groups and was heard frequently at hoots. A powerful rendition was given by Tom Makem at The Newport Folk Festival in 1960. His performance is preserved in Volume 1 of the Vanguard albums made at the festival (VRS 9083).

Rich Gal, Poor Gal

Rich gal she wears the____ best per - fume; Poor gal she'd like to wear the same;____ My gal she don't wear a dog - gone thing; But I love her just the same.____ I'm go - in' 'cross the plains, charm - in' Bet - sy.____ I'm go - in' 'cross the moun - tains, Cor - a - lee.____ And

if I nev - er see you a - gain

Great God, re - mem - ber me.____

Rich gal she smells like her sweet perfume.
Poor gal her smell is a shame.
My gal she smells like an old billy goat—
But it's her smell just the same.

Rich gal she rides in a big Cadillac.
Poor gal she drives a Model A.
My gal she only has to wave her thumb,
And she gets there right away.

Rich gal she lives in a big brick house.
Poor gal she lives in a frame.
My gal she lives in the Nashville jail—
But it's a brick house just the same.

Here's an old hillbilly favorite that has long been popular
with city-billies, too—particularly those found on the
campus. It calls for a good jump-tempo, country harmonizing on the choruses—and some fancy banjo work in
between and behind the singing won't hurt a bit. Some
people use an E flat diminished chord in the eleventh
measure, but I prefer the F chord. If you have trouble
in this key, try D (C becomes D, G7 becomes A7, F becomes G, C7 becomes D7, and Fm becomes Gm), a very
easy key for guitar. If you want to hear it performed,
you can look around for some old hillbilly recordings by
artists like the Louvin Brothers, or listen to The Limeliters *Sing Out!* album (LPM 2445).

My Last Gold Dollar

I wish I had nev-er been born, or had died when I___ was young, I wish I nev-er had kissed your sweet red lips or lis-tened to your ly - ing tongue. Oh, my last gold dol-lar is gone, Oh, my last gold dol-lar is gone, My board bill's due and my whis-key bill, too, Oh, my last gold dol-lar is gone.

Oh, I'll never drink whiskey no more,
Oh, I'll never drink whiskey no more,
I'll lay me head in the barroom door,
And I'll shout when I get happy, Lord, Lord.

Oh, baby, six months ain't so long.
Oh, baby, six months ain't so long.
Six months are gone, six more a-comin' on,
Oh, baby, six months ain't so long.

This is another one of those hillbilly songs made up out of verses from other songs or from which other songs have been fabricated. Somebody has an awful job on his hands trying to figure out which came first. In the meantime, you can have a lot of fun with the song itself, particularly if you can round up a good fiddle and banjo player to back you up.

Here We Go, Baby

WORDS BY MARVIN MOORE

Chorus

Here we go, ba - by, down the road.

Here we go, ba - by, down the road.

Here we go, ba - by, down the road.

Here we go, ba - by, down the road.

Verse

Wish I had a need - le, As fine as I could sew, I'd sew my ba - by to my side And down the road we'd go.

I'll always love my baby
Until the day I die.
The way my baby loves me
Makes me laugh and cry.

Chorus:

Here we go, baby, all the time.
Here we go, baby, all the time.
Here we go, baby, all the time.
Here we go, baby, all the time.

Wish I was an apple,
Hangin' from a tree.
And baby she would pluck me off
And take a bite of me.

Chorus:

Here we go, baby, summertime,
Here we go, baby, wintertime,
Here we go, baby, springtime,
Here we go, baby, all the time.

Ain't no girl that's sweeter,
Ain't no girl so true,
As my baby all the time,
That's why I love you.

Repeat previous chorus.

It used to be a custom to give song books elaborate and
flowery titles. One of the longest titles I have ever seen
was on a book printed privately in 1927 by John and
Evelyn McCutcheon: THE ISLAND SONG BOOK Be-
ing a small COLLECTION of our favorite BALLADS,
ANTHEMS, LULLABIES AND DIRGES Of *This Par-
ticular Section* of the BAHAMA ISLANDS And Also
SUCH OTHER DITTIES As have seemed Befitting by
Reason of their *Piratical, Nautical* or *Sentimental* Appeal
Together with Several *Local* and *Topical Lays* Relating
Only to TREASURE ISLAND To which is prefix'd An
Explanatory and *Historical Introduction* To which is
added A Number of SKETCHES and PHOTOGRAPHS
Illustrative of Same.

The book contained many discoveries, priceless to a
folksong collector, among which "Here We Go Baby"
was one of my favorites. Only a fragment was presented
in the book. Over the years I added verses and found the
tune changing as I performed it, until this version had
evolved—calypso style, naturally.

The House Carpenter

Pepys Ballads, printed in 1685, contains "A Warning for Married Women, being an example of Mrs. Jane Reynolds (a West-country woman), born near Plymouth, who, having plighted her troth to a Seaman, was afterwards married to a Carpenter, and at last carried away by a Spirit, the manner how shall presently be recited. To a West-country tune . . ." It is one of the earliest printed versions of "The House Carpenter" or "James Harris" or "The Daemon Lover." It is another one of the great ballads in the Child collection (243) that has a strong tradition in Britain and America.

"Well met, well met, my own true love, Well met, well met", cried he, "I've just re - turned from the salt, salt sea, And it's all for the sake of thee."

"Oh, I could have married the king's daughter fair,
And she would have married me.
But I have refused the crown of gold,
And it's all for the sake of thee."

"If you could have married the king's daughter dear,
I'm sure you are to blame,
For I am married to the house carpenter
And he is a fine young man."

"If you'll forsake your house carpenter
And come away with me,
I'll take you to where the grass grows green
On the banks of Italy."

"If I forsake my house carpenter
And come away with thee,
What have you got to support me on
And keep me from slavery?"

"I have six ships on the salt, salt sea,
A-sailing for dry land,
And a hundred and twenty jolly young lads
Shall be at thy command."

She picked up her poor little babe;
Her kisses were one, two, three,
Saying, "Stay here with my house carpenter
And keep him company."

They had not been at sea two weeks,
I'm sure it was not three,
When this poor maid began to weep,
And she wept most bitterly.

"Oh, do you weep for your gold?" he said,
"Your houses, your land or your store?"
"No, I do weep for my poor little babe
That I shall see no more."

They had not been at sea three weeks,
I'm sure it was not four,
When in the ship there sprang a leak,
And she sank to rise no more.

"Farewell, farewell, my own true love,
Farewell, farewell," cried she,
"Oh, I have deserted my house carpenter
For a grave in the depths of the sea."

Oh, cursed be the sea-going train,
And all the sailors' lives,
For the robbing of the house carpenter,
And the taking away of his wife.

Little Phoebe

"Little Phoebe" is a contemporary version of the Father Grumble song, which has a long tradition in Britain and America. For different versions listen to Bob Gibson (Stinson, SLP 76), Pete Seeger's "Equinoxial" (Folkways, FA 2452), and Ellen Stekert (Stinson, SLP 49).

E-qui-nox-ial swore by the green leaves on the trees, trees, that he could do more work in a day than Phoe-be could in three, three, That he could do more work in a day than Phoe-be could in three.

Little Phoebe standing there and this is what she said:
"You can do the work in the house and I'll go follow the plow, plow,
You can do the work in the house and I'll go follow the plow."

Continue, as above

"And you must milk the brindle cow that stands in yonder stall;

And you must feed that little pig that stands in yonder
sty.

"And you must churn that crock of cream that I left
in the frame;
And you must watch the fat in the pot or it'll go in a
flame.

"And you must wind that hank of yarn that I spun
yesterday;
And you must watch that speckled hen so she won't run
astray."

Little Phoebe took her whip and went to follow the
plow;
And Equinoxial took the pail and went to milk the cow.

The brindle cow she turned around and wrinkled up her
nose;
And gave him a dip upon the lip and the blood ran to his
toes.

He went to feed the little pig that stands in yonder sty;
He bumped his nose upon the beam and how the blood
did fly.

He went to churn that crock of cream that she left in
the frame;
And he forgot the fat in the pot and it all went in a
flame.

He went to wind that hank of yarn that she spun
yesterday;
But he forgot that speckled hen and so she ran away.

He looked to the east; he looked to the west; and saw
the setting sun.
He swore it had been an awful long day and Phoebe
hadn't come.

Then little Phoebe came and saw him looking sad;
She clapped her hands upon her sides and swore that
she was glad.

Hagnaleena

I learned this crazy mixed-up song from Bryce Pfanenstiel of Redwood City, California and Jane Brenner of San Francisco. Bryce was exposed to it first at the Sigma Nu frat house at the University of Kansas, in 1955, and Jane caught it at Camp Akita in Ohio, in 1948. Once you get the simple format in hand the real fun begins when you try to keep up a frantic pace to your own made-up verses. Good for guitar or ukulele, but the latter instrument seems to be made just for this song. The verses given here deal with her eyes, hair and teeth. The rest of her anatomy is up to you.

She had two eyes in her head;
One was green and one was red.

Chorus

Hag - na - leen - a, Mag - na - leen - a,
Hoot - en - steim - er What - en - teim - er,
Hog - an Log - an Blog - an was her name.

She had some hair on her back;
Some was orange and some was black.

She had two teeth in her mouth;
One went north and the other went south.